Contents

C000243768

Answers

Published by CGP

ISBN: 978 1 78294 803 2

Pages 4-6 contain public sector information licensed under the Open Government Licence v3.0.
http://www.nationalarchives.gov.uk/doc/open-government-licence/version/3/

www.cgpbooks.co.uk
Printed by Elanders Ltd, Newcastle upon Tyne.
Clipart from Corel®
Cover image: © iStock.com/FrankRamspott

Text, design, layout and original illustrations © Coordination Group Publications Ltd. (CGP) 2017

All rights reserved.

About

About This Book

This is the matching answer book to our Maths for Key Stage 2 Year 6 Textbook.

Here you'll find a Programme of Study mapping, showing where each Year 6 requirement is covered in the Textbook. This makes it easy for you to find the pages in the Textbook you need for your lesson.

There is also a Scheme of Work which suggests the order you might want your pupils to work through the book during the school year. This uses 11-week terms so that additional weeks in each term can be used for assessment or other activities.

Finally, there are answers to every question in the Textbook.

About The Textbook

The Textbook is split into eight sections, with each one covering a different area of the Year 6 Programme of Study. These sections are:

- Section 1 — Number and Place Value
- Section 2 — Calculations
- Section 3 — Fractions and Decimals
- Section 4 — Ratio and Proportion

- Section 5 — Algebra
- Section 6 — Measurement
- Section 7 — Geometry
- Section 8 — Statistics

Within each section, all of the statutory requirements from the corresponding Programme of Study area (as well as the important non-statutory requirements) are covered. Many of the requirements are covered across several pages. This is done so that every part of each requirement is covered in depth, and the most important topics can be revisited in multiple lessons.

Topic Pages

The main topic pages start with one to three examples. These are to give pupils a brief visual reminder of how to approach some of the questions.

The questions are split into three differentiated Sets which can be assigned to pupils depending on their ability.

- Set A is for pupils working towards the expected level for Year 6.
- Set B is for pupils working at the expected level for Year 6.
- Set C is for pupils working above the expected level for Year 6.

At the end of each topic, there is a learning objective summarising the Programme of Study requirements covered in that topic. There are tick boxes here for pupils to show how confident they feel with the topic.

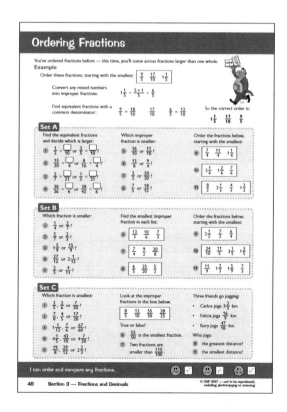

About

Review Pages

After every few topics, there is a Review page with more questions on those topics. The questions cover the full range of difficulty from the main topic pages, but are not split into differentiated Sets, so every pupil can try all the questions.

The Review pages are really useful for recapping and summarising several topics within one lesson.

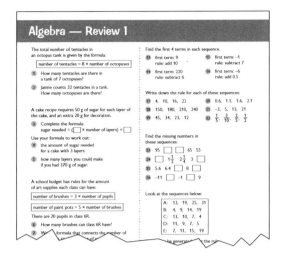

Challenge Pages

At the end of each section, there are Challenge pages. These have a different style to the rest of the book — the questions test pupils' deeper understanding of the maths topics in the section. Pupils might have to investigate something, talk to a friend about a problem, or play a game. Like the review pages, the questions are not differentiated.

Answers are provided for Challenges where possible, but are not included for open-ended tasks and games.

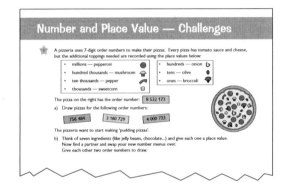

Online Resources

On our website, you can access free printable resources that can be used with different questions throughout the book. The resources contain things such as blank coordinate grids, which will save pupils having to copy them out.

To access these resources, go to:

www.cgpbooks.co.uk/KS2MathsResources

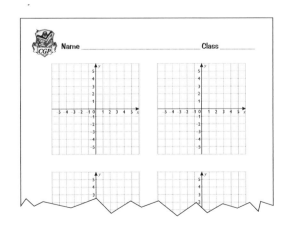

Programme of Study Mapping

A mapping from the Year 6 Programme of Study to the pages of our Maths for Key Stage 2 Year 6 Textbook is given on the next three pages. As well as all of the statutory points from the Programme of Study, some important non-statutory points have also been included — these are marked with an asterisk*.

Number and Place Value

read, write, order and compare numbers up to 10 000 000 and determine the value of each digit	2, 3, 6
round any whole number to a required degree of accuracy	7
use negative numbers in context, and calculate intervals across 0	4
solve number and practical problems that involve all of the above	8, 9
Number and place value review pages	*5, 10*
Number and place value challenges	*11, 12*

Addition, Subtraction, Multiplication and Division

multiply multi-digit numbers up to 4 digits by a two-digit whole number using the formal written method of long multiplication	26
divide numbers up to 4 digits by a two-digit whole number using the formal written method of long division, and interpret remainders as whole number remainders, fractions, or by rounding, as appropriate for the context	28, 29
divide numbers up to 4 digits by a two-digit number using the formal written method of short division where appropriate, interpreting remainders according to the context	27
perform mental calculations, including with mixed operations and large numbers	13, 14, 20-23
identify common factors, common multiples and prime numbers	31, 32
use their knowledge of the order of operations to carry out calculations involving the 4 operations	33, 34
solve addition and subtraction multi-step problems in contexts, deciding which operations and methods to use and why	17, 18
solve problems involving addition, subtraction, multiplication and division	22, 23, 39-42
use estimation to check answers to calculations and determine, in the context of a problem, an appropriate degree of accuracy	37, 38
*practise addition and subtraction for larger numbers using formal written methods	15, 16
*practise multiplication using formal written methods	25
*round answers to a specified degree of accuracy	36
Calculations review pages	*19, 24, 30, 35, 43*
Calculations challenges	*44-46*

Programme of Study Mapping

Fractions (including decimals and percentages)

use common factors to simplify fractions; use common multiples to express fractions in the same denomination	47
compare and order fractions, including fractions > 1	48
add and subtract fractions with different denominators and mixed numbers, using the concept of equivalent fractions	49-52
multiply simple pairs of proper fractions, writing the answer in its simplest form	54
divide proper fractions by whole numbers	55
associate a fraction with division and calculate decimal fraction equivalents for a simple fraction	63
identify the value of each digit in numbers given to 3 decimal places and multiply and divide numbers by 10, 100 and 1000 giving answers up to 3 decimal places	57, 58
multiply one-digit numbers with up to 2 decimal places by whole numbers	60
use written division methods in cases where the answer has up to 2 decimal places	61, 62
solve problems which require answers to be rounded to specified degrees of accuracy	64, 65
recall and use equivalences between simple fractions, decimals and percentages, including in different contexts	66, 67
*use the relationship between unit fractions and division to work backwards by multiplying a quantity that represents a unit fraction to find the whole quantity	56
Fractions and decimals review pages	*53, 59, 68*
Fractions and decimals challenges	*69-71*

Ratio and Proportion

solve problems involving the relative sizes of 2 quantities where missing values can be found by using integer multiplication and division facts	72-74
solve problems involving the calculation of percentages [for example, of measures and such as 15% of 360] and the use of percentages for comparison	80, 81
solve problems involving similar shapes where the scale factor is known or can be found	78, 79
solve problems involving unequal sharing and grouping using knowledge of fractions and multiples	75, 76
Ratio and proportion review pages	*77, 82*
Ratio and proportion challenges	*83, 84*

Algebra

use simple formulae	85-87
generate and describe linear number sequences	88, 89
express missing number problems algebraically	91, 92
find pairs of numbers that satisfy an equation with 2 unknowns	93, 94
enumerate possibilities of combinations of 2 variables	93, 94
Algebra review pages	*90, 95*
Algebra challenges	*96-98*

Programme of Study Mapping

Measurement

solve problems involving the calculation and conversion of units of measure, using decimal notation up to 3 decimal places where appropriate	103, 104
use, read, write and convert between standard units, converting measurements of length, mass, volume and time from a smaller unit of measure to a larger unit, and vice versa, using decimal notation to up to 3 decimal places	99, 101, 102
convert between miles and kilometres	100
recognise that shapes with the same areas can have different perimeters and vice versa	110, 111
recognise when it is possible to use formulae for area and volume of shapes	106-109, 113-116
calculate the area of parallelograms and triangles	106-109
calculate, estimate and compare volume of cubes and cuboids using standard units, including cubic centimetres (cm³) and cubic metres (m³), and extending to other units	113-116
Measurement review pages	*105, 112, 117*
Measurement challenges	*118, 119*

Geometry

draw 2-D shapes using given dimensions and angles	128-133
recognise, describe and build simple 3-D shapes, including making nets	139-141
compare and classify geometric shapes based on their properties and sizes and find unknown angles in any triangles, quadrilaterals, and regular polygons	120-124, 135, 136, 139
illustrate and name parts of circles, including radius, diameter and circumference and know that the diameter is twice the radius	137, 138
recognise angles where they meet at a point, are on a straight line, or are vertically opposite, and find missing angles	125, 126
describe positions on the full coordinate grid (all 4 quadrants)	143, 144
draw and translate simple shapes on the coordinate plane, and reflect them in the axes	147-150
*draw and label rectangles (including squares), parallelograms and rhombuses, specified by coordinates in the four quadrants, predicting missing coordinates using the properties of shapes	145, 146
Geometry review pages	*127, 134, 142, 151*
Geometry challenges	*152-154*

Statistics

interpret and construct pie charts and line graphs and use these to solve problems	155-158, 160-163
calculate and interpret the mean as an average	164, 165
Statistics review pages	*159, 166*
Statistics challenges	*167, 168*

Scheme of Work

This Scheme of Work can be used alongside the Year 6 Textbook to cover the Year 6 Programme of Study in full. Each term is divided into **11** weeks.

All statutory requirements are covered by Week 3 of Summer term — Weeks 4-11 have no suggested topics to allow for recapping of material in preparation for KS3, and end-of-year activities.

Term 1 — Autumn

Week	Topic	Page
1	Place Value	2
	Writing Numbers	3
	Negative Numbers	4
	Number and Place Value — Review 1	*5*
2	Ordering Numbers	6
	Rounding Numbers	7
	Solving Problems with Numbers	8, 9
	Number and Place Value — Review 2	*10*
	Number and Place Value — Challenges	*11, 12*
3	Mental Addition	13
	Mental Subtraction	14
	Written Addition	15
	Written Subtraction	16
	Addition and Subtraction Problems	17, 18
	Calculations — Review 1	*19*
4	Mental Multiplication	20
	Mental Division	21
	Mental Calculation Problems	22, 23
	Short Multiplication	25
	Calculations — Review 2	*24*
5	Long Multiplication	26
	Short Division	27
	Long Division — 1	28
	Long Division — 2	29
	Calculations — Review 3	*30*
6	Common Factors	31
	Common Multiples	32
	BODMAS — 1	33
	BODMAS — 2	34
	Calculations — Review 4	*35*
7	Rounding Answers	36
	Checking Calculations	37, 38
	Calculation Problems — 1	39, 40
	Calculation Problems — 2	41, 42
	Calculations — Review 5	*43*
	Calculations — Challenges	*44-46*
8	Simplifying Fractions	47
	Ordering Fractions	48
	Adding Fractions — 1	49
	Adding Fractions — 2	50

Scheme of Work

Term 1 — Autumn (continued)

Term 2 — Spring

Scheme of Work

Term 2 — Spring (continued)

Term 3 — Summer

Section 1 — Number and Place Value

Page 2: Place Value

Set A

1. 2 hundred thousands or 200 000
2. 9 thousands or 9000
3. 3 millions or 3 000 000
4. 7 ten thousands or 70 000
5. 5 hundreds or 500
6. 6 ones or 6
7. 1 ten or 10
8. 1
9. 7
10. 3
11. 9
12. 3 812 745
13. 4 712 835
14. 4 852 731

Set B

1. 3 millions or 3 000 000
2. 4 tens or 40
3. 6 hundred thousands or 600 000
4. 2 millions or 2 000 000
5. 7 thousands or 7000
6. 5 ten thousands or 50 000
7. 3 millions or 3 000 000
   3 ten thousands or 30 000
   3 tens or 30
8. 8 hundred thousands or 800 000
   2 thousands or 2000
   4 hundreds or 400
   6 ones or 6
9. 7 millions or 7 000 000
   7 hundred thousands or 700 000
   3 ten thousands or 30 000
   1 thousand or 1000
   9 tens or 90
10. 7 003 985
11. 2 ten thousands or 20 000

Set C

1. 8 thousands or 8000
2. 4 tens or 40
3. 8 ten thousands or 80 000
4. 7 hundred thousands or 700 000
5. 3 millions or 3 000 000
6. 9 ones or 9
7. 7 hundreds or 700
8. 3 052 467
9. 2 807 064
10. 8 660 408
11. 9 875 421
12. 1 245 789
13. 9 999 999
14. 10 000 000

Page 3: Writing Numbers

Set A

1. 300 000
2. 500 617
3. 7 000 000
4. 1 200 000
5. 6 000 059
6. four million
7. nine million, nine hundred thousand
8. four million, one hundred and forty
9. three million, five hundred and four thousand, four hundred
10. one million, two hundred thousand, five hundred and sixty-seven
11. eight million, forty-five thousand, eight hundred
12. 2 510 490
13. four million, four hundred and eighty-five thousand, two hundred and nineteen

Set B

1. 6 973 142
2. 9 129 790
3. 3 212 813
4. nine million, eight hundred thousand, two hundred and thirty-seven
5. four million, seven hundred and thirty-five thousand, four hundred
6. eight million, four hundred and ninety-three thousand, seven hundred and thirty-eight

   one million, four hundred and ninety-three thousand, seven hundred and twenty-nine

   nine million, four hundred and ninety-two thousand, seven hundred and nineteen
7. 6 500 096
   8 600 024
   4 500 063

Set C

1. 5 844 862
2. 9 295 090
3. 17 638 040
4. 30 052 112
5. seven million, three hundred and four thousand, four hundred and ninety-four
6. nine million, four hundred and ninety-five thousand and forty-nine
7. nine million, three hundred and four thousand, four hundred and thirty-four

   eight million, three hundred and forty-eight thousand, four hundred and ninety-one

   twelve million, three hundred and four thousand, four hundred and ninety-eight
8. 3 671 000
9. 8 673 713
10. fourteen million, one hundred and sixty thousand, four hundred and sixty-seven

Page 4: Negative Numbers

Set A

1. 18 m
2. 25 m
3. 35 cm
4. 70 cm
5. 60 cm
6. 10 cm

Set B

1. −6 °C
2. 3 °C
3. 12 °C
4. 21 °C
5. 22 °C
6. 13 °C
7. 57 °C
8. 77 °C
9. 14 °C

Set C

1. 350 m
2. 5000 m
3. 196 °C
4. 172 °C
5. the fish fingers

Page 5: Number and Place Value — Review 1

1. 7 ten thousands or 70 000
2. 3 millions or 3 000 000
3. 2 thousands or 2000
4. 6 tens or 60
5. 9 ones or 9
6. 5 hundreds or 500
7. 3 hundred thousands or 300 000
8. 1 thousand or 1000
9. 9 hundred thousands or 900 000
10. 3 tens or 30
11. 6 millions or 6 000 000
12. 7 ten thousands or 70 000
13. 6 hundred thousands or 600 000
14. 5 thousands or 5000
15. 4 ones or 4
16. 8 hundreds or 800
17. 6 295 831
18. 8 235 691
19. 6 135 892
20. 9 865 321
21. 1 235 689
22. 5 600 030
23. 6 532 180
24. 7 864 222
25. 9 047 631
26. eight million
27. seven million, eight hundred thousand
28. three million, three hundred and forty-five thousand
29. two million, six hundred and thirty thousand, seven hundred
30. one million, one hundred and fifty thousand, eight hundred and fifty
31. eight million, fifty-three thousand and five hundred
32. five million, six hundred and twenty-nine thousand, seven hundred and twenty
33. four million, eight hundred and thirty thousand, two hundred and seventy-three
34. 5 730 106
35. 9 422 583
36. 6 954 173
37. 3 050 000
38. three million, three hundred and fifty thousand
39. 2 079 976
40. two million, nineteen thousand, four hundred and seventy-six
41. −1.9 °C
42. £630
43. £1160
44. £1410
45. £70

Page 6: Ordering Numbers

Set A

1. 5 989 932
2. 5 231 724
3. 3 982 101
4. 7 498 014
5. 1 285 942
6. 9 748 294
7. >
8. >
9. <
10. >
11. >
12. <
13. 3 234 596, 4 582 834, 4 731 984, 5 750 519
14. 9 720 482, 9 155 343, 8 717 086, 8 115 898

Set B

1. <
2. <
3. <
4. >
5. >
6. >
7. 9 458 106
8. 1 639 788
9. 2 966 311
10. 7 935 351
11. 3 007 641, 3 199 334, 3 688 909, 3 761 490, 4 097 518, 4 491 916
12. 8 043 087, 8 113 041, 8 245 613, 8 763 207, 8 881 088, 8 897 512

Set C

1. 7 380 626
2. 8 274 389
3. 1 873 157
4. 7 252 307
5. 8 or 9
6. 1 or 2
7. 8 or 9
8. 8 or 9
9. 7, 8 or 9
10. 0, 1 or 2
11. 1 or 2
12. Blayd
13. Glorio

Page 7: Rounding Numbers

Set A

1. 931 270
2. 931 300
3. 931 000
4. 7 700 000
5. 8 000 000
6. 1 564 000
7. 2 697 000
8. 7 794 000
9. 4 350 000
10. 8 510 000
11. 6 568 932
12. 6 569 000

Set B

1. 8 898 000
2. 8 897 800
3. 8 900 000
4. 3 000 000
5. 3 050 000
6. 5 258 320
   5 258 300
   5 260 000
7. 5 269 997
   5 269 995
8. 100 000
9. 10 000
10. 10 000
11. 100 000
12. 10 000
13. 100 000

Set C

1. 4 075 000, 4 080 000, 4 100 000
2. 2 218 000, 2 220 000, 2 200 000
3. 7 291 000, 7 290 000, 7 300 000
4. 3 029 650, 3 029 700, 3 000 000
5. 8 435 310, 8 435 300, 8 000 000
6. 100
7. 100 000
8. 1 000 000
9. 10
10. 1000
11. 10 000
12. 1000
13. 4 366 810, 4 366 800, 4 367 000, 4 370 000, 4 400 000, 4 000 000
14. £2 549 999

Pages 8-9: Solving Problems with Numbers

Set A

1. C and D
2. A and E
3. eight million, two hundred and ninety-two thousand
4. five million, four hundred and ten thousand
5. 45 m
6. 60 m
7. 39.5 m
8. £55
9. £780
10. £1250
11. 28
12. 15
13. 27

Set B

1. 8000
2. 100 000
3. 7 000 000
4. 7 439 216
5. 7 400 000 or 7 439 200
6. fossil, vase, diamond, armour, coin
7. 8 m
8. 45 m
9. 30 m
10. 15 days

Set C

1. eight million, six hundred and fifty-nine thousand, four hundred and forty-one
2. six million, nine hundred and fourteen thousand, eight hundred and fifty-four
3. eight million, one hundred and forty-four thousand, five hundred and sixty-nine
4. 5 hours
5. 40 hours
6. 65 hours
7. £7 937 000, £7 900 000, £8 000 000
8. banana bread, brownies, cookies, cupcakes, sausage rolls
9. 20 million or 20 000 000
10. every number is rounded up to the nearest million, so the estimate has to be over the true value
11. 9 499 999 and 8 500 000
12. 136 students

Page 10: Number and Place Value — Review 2

1. 7 201 796
2. 4 362 896
3. 2 426 749
4. 3 753 753
5. 5 899 750
6. 7 156 947
7. 8 258 552
8. 9 688 929
9. >
10. <
11. >
12. <
13. 4 755 104, 4 649 116, 4 644 371, 4 638 052
14. 5 234 596, 5 501 819, 5 525 178, 5 573 452
15. 2 683 663
16. 9 819 006
17. 7 602 420
18. 6 392 000
19. 6 392 100
20. 6 400 000
21. 6 000 000
22. 3 000 000
23. 2 000 000
24. 8 000 000
25. 6 000 000
26. 6 590 000
27. 8 030 000
28. 1 180 000
29. 2 870 000
30. 7 461 072
31. £8 453 900, £8 454 000, £8 500 000
32. £4 000 000
33. 6 499 999 and 5 500 000
34. 64 m
35. see column below:

Change
6 °C
11 °C
10 °C
7 °C
20 °C

36. 2 600 000
37. four million, five hundred and fifty-four thousand, six hundred and forty

Pages 11-12: Number and Place Value — Challenges

1. a) 756 484 should have 7 mushroom, 5 pepper, 6 sweetcorn, 4 onion, 8 olives and 4 broccoli
   3 160 729 should have 3 pepperoni, 1 mushroom, 6 pepper, 7 onion, 2 olives and 9 broccoli
   4 000 723 should have 4 pepperoni, 7 onion, 2 olives and 3 broccoli
3. Koala = 6 999 995 mg
   Platypus = 2 193 104 mg
   Quoll = 2 803 351 mg
   Echidna = 6 330 570 mg
4. Radiceville: one million, eight hundred thousand
   1 800 000
   Williamsberg: one million, eight hundred thousand
   1 800 000
   Challinorth: three million, eight hundred thousand
   3 800 000
   Fairburntown: six hundred thousand
   600 000
5. a) Styria and Ocragua
   b) 625 °C
   c) 30 °C
   d) −35 °C
   e) Yes
6. a) nine million, three hundred and twenty-six thousand, five hundred and eighty-six
   b) four million, three hundred and seventeen thousand, three hundred and two
   c) five million, one hundred and twenty-four thousand, three hundred and forty-five
   d) eight million, seventy-four thousand, one hundred and ninety-two
   e) nine hundred and forty-two thousand, one hundred and thirty-seven

Section 2 — Calculations

Page 13: Mental Addition

Set A

1. 34 000	8. 82 710	15. 15 000
2. 93 000	9. 770 000	16. 40 000
3. 240 400	10. 902 400	17. 70 000
4. 961 000	11. 980 500	18. 3 000 000
5. 9 100 000	12. 6 470 090	19. 2 200 000
6. 8 480 000	13. 7 480 000	20. 6 000 600
7. 9 710 030	14. 6 640 800	21. 4 002 000

Set B

1. 810 500	8. 520 000	15. 310 000
2. 900 250	9. 716 000	16. 201 000
3. 183 000	10. 1 229 000	17. 180 000
4. 6 170 000	11. 6 804 100	18. 2 400 000
5. 8 690 000	12. 6 320 800	19. 4 000 200
6. 7 950 000	13. 6 305 000	20. 3 040 000
7. 8 300 470	14. 9 200 120	21. 910 000

Set C

1. 230 500	8. 1 095 000	15. 205 000
2. 1 300 370	9. 1 319 000	16. 450 000
3. 6 520 014	10. 1 251 000	17. 800 090
4. 9 050 000	11. 5 500 036	18. 2 007 000
5. 8 031 600	12. 7 400 010	19. 800 060
6. 9 855 000	13. 7 100 135	20. 200 040
7. 8 900 110	14. 9 155 000	21. 6 080 000

Page 14: Mental Subtraction

Set A

1. 50 000	8. 33 000	15. 50 000
2. 38 000	9. 20 070	16. 10 000
3. 426 000	10. 255 000	17. 203 000
4. 180 400	11. 305 500	18. 600 200
5. 4 200 000	12. 1 500 600	19. 200 000
6. 2 400 000	13. 2 040 080	20. 4 000 500
7. 7 625 000	14. 6 610 000	21. 7 010 000

Set B

1. 230 000	8. 850 000	15. 110 000
2. 1 187 000	9. 930 400	16. 200 000
3. 299 000	10. 5 500 030	17. 200 100
4. 1 900 000	11. 380 000	18. 500 000
5. 1 927 000	12. 185 000	19. 3 800 000
6. 3 700 200	13. 900 400	20. 500 050
7. 6 050 500	14. 1 324 600	21. 5 900 000

Set C

1. 380 000	8. 358 000	15. 90 000
2. 3 725 000	9. 588 000	16. 240 000
3. 1 960 000	10. 79 000	17. 700 000
4. 557 000	11. 7 869 200	18. 909 000
5. 3 610 520	12. 1 842 000	19. 5 060 000
6. 3 408 000	13. 370 000	20. 870 000
7. 4 905 000	14. 690	21. 6 009 001

Page 15: Written Addition

Set A

1. 42 957	6. 5 962 938	10. 963 914
2. 889 189	7. 61 973	11. 6 796 583
3. 4671.9	8. 968 637	12. 7 438 784
4. 978 589	9. 879 878	13. 7 374 398
5. 2591.36		

Set B

1. 866 983	5. 96 380.97	8. 873 959.9
2. 8581.78	6. 8944.691	9. 9 948 644
3. 9764.76	7. 8 668 622	10. 6 286 293
4. 7 465 572		

Set C

1. 847 697	5. 9 955 164	9. 956 091
2. 16 246.26	6. 784 982.6	10. 4 387 790
3. 4 815 898	7. 9 938.204	11. 4 955 591
4. 9 170 686	8. 1 164 918	12. 6 928 059

Page 16: Written Subtraction

Set A

1. 14 755	6. 3 108 352	10. 3 515.3
2. 223 153	7. 135 122	11. 520 111.2
3. 13 214.5	8. 433 442	12. 2 424 724
4. 26 232.2	9. 214 632	13. 4 083 325
5. 1 156 252		

Set B

1. 124 193	5. 1 427 252	8. 1 923 115
2. 232 162	6. 584 186.3	9. 327 482
3. 30 642.32	7. 144 531.3	10. £513 015.42
4. 167 242.2		

Set C

1. 564 231	6. 6 269 530	10. 692 076.04
2. 521 516	7. 84 837.384	11. £224 048.09
3. 134 353.5	8. 15 232.26	12. 7 140 916
4. 741 153	9. 4 433 831	13. 4 927 908
5. 1817.195		

Pages 17-18: Addition and Subtraction Problems

Set A

1. £445 542
2. 79 995 km
3. 200 005 km
4. 131 420
5. 184 020
6. 51 400
7. 5 573 633
8. 5 524 334
9. Team 1, by 49 299
10. 1 217 284
11. 4 015 220
12. 6 419 628

Set B

1. 777 734
2. 105 208
3. 1 078 942
4. 990 218.9 g
5. 38 122.9 g
6. 719 746.3 g
7. 361 366
8. 600 030 cm
9. 207 352
10. 7 388 001

Set C

1. 805 100
2. 6 060 965
3. 1 495 015
4. 3 199 564
5. 704.744 − 484.639 = 220.105
6. 1351.578 + 2495.808 = 3847.386
7. £405 778
8. £2 394 515
9. £3 609 895

Page 19: Calculations — Review 1

1. 45 000
2. 900 300
3. 2 570 000
4. 3 276 000
5. 6 814 000
6. 5 510 000
7. 7 109 000
8. 8 800 100
9. 4 110 048
10. 3 211 004
11. 2 100 000
12. 600 000
13. 90 000
14. 1 000 800
15. 909 009
16. 42 000
17. 630 200
18. 6 300 000
19. 4 400 000
20. 500 000
21. 8 680 000
22. 6 300 440
23. 1 522 100
24. 2 598 000
25. 3 598 150
26. 20 000
27. 1 000 500
28. 3 000 015
29. 1 170 000
30. 8060
31. 788 889
32. 7 391 580
33. 114 580.99
34. 16 683.118
35. 659 990
36. 8 447 969
37. 9 181.99
38. 3 293 583
39. 9 636 823
40. 557 043.89
41. 5 418 922
42. 9 877 220
43. 9 084 204
44. 40 000.106
45. 610 525
46. 3 130 450
47. 52 649.62
48. 1 546 868
49. 343 313
50. 1 385 547
51. 59 056.5
52. 1 841 185
53. 7 464 781
54. 9167.97
55. 3 865 756
56. 4 636 577
57. 533 647.28
58. 1 787 475
59. 3 101 700
60. 6 253 700
61. 50 300
62. 1 472 601
63. 9 708 177

Page 20: Mental Multiplication

Set A

1. 1800
2. 2000
3. 5600
4. 9000
5. 80 000
6. 630 000
7. 300 000
8. 8, 240, 240, 5840
9. 3, 270, 270, 870
10. 1150
11. 1440
12. 3648
13. 3030
14. 29 200
15. 31 200
16. 11 900

Set B

1. 3600
2. 14 000
3. 33 000
4. 240 000
5. 270 000
6. 4 200 000
7. 238 000
8. 720 000
9. 760 000
10. 12 840
11. 450 540
12. 468 000
13. 2 400 000
14. 1890
15. 4520p

Set C

1. 360 000
2. 420 000
3. 150 000
4. 720 000
5. 72 000
6. 88 000
7. 55 200
8. 722 400
9. 495 000
10. 75 900
11. 539 000
12. 4 520 000
13. 168 hours
14. 10 080 minutes
15. 7590 seconds

Page 21: Mental Division

Set A

1. 6, 60
2. 7, 700
3. 9, 120
4. 90
5. 110
6. 600
7. 8
8. 80
9. 60
10. 70
11. 800
12. 300
13. 900
14. 900
15. 90
16. 70
17. 70

Set B

1. 90
2. 90
3. 11 000
4. 1200
5. 9000
6. 110
7. 6
8. 90
9. 60
10. 1200
11. 700
12. 80 000
13. 300
14. 600 kg

Set C

1. 20
2. 90
3. 60
4. 11
5. 7
6. 50
7. 7000
8. 4000
9. 120 000
10. 1100
11. 600
12. 90 000
13. £900
14. 10 000 chains

Pages 22-23: Mental Calculation Problems

Set A

1. 9600
2. 200
3. 640 000
4. 1 280 000
5. 80 000
6. 1760
7. 30
8. 100
9. £1 210 000
10. 731 000
11. 21 300

Set B

1.

	Number of cakes	Slices per cake	Number of slices
Chocolate	200	8	1600
Carrot	230	6	1380
Fruit	120	12	1440

2. £263 085
3. 92 465
4. 200 000
5. 48 465
6. 13 916
7. 8000
8. 12 420
9. 108 000
10. 67 994

Set C

1. 1 170 000 m
2. £64 430
3. 9190
4. 1100
5. 144 000 g
6. 1200
7. 2 700 000
8. 90 000
9. £9 960 000

Page 24: Calculations — Review 2

1. 4800
2. 1800
3. 400 000
4. 280 000
5. 360 000
6. 630 000
7. 240 000
8. 360 000
9. 560 000
10. 350 000
11. 72 000
12. 88 000
13. 13 200
14. 14 400
15. 6,
    120,
    120, 3120
16. 7200,
    9,
    7200, 7560
17. 520
18. 810
19. 900
20. 3720
21. 1480
22. 38 500
23. 378 000
24. 752 000
25. 77 099
26. 765 000
27. 376 000
28. 117 600
29. 6640
30. £432
31. 144 000
32. 60
33. 800
34. 7
35. 11
36. 90
37. 90
38. 120
39. 700
40. 90
41. 80
42. 120
43. 110
44. 70
45. 90
46. 6,
    900
47. 12,
    800
48. 3000
49. 6000
50. 60 000
51. 60 000
52. 800
53. 900
54. 600
55. 800
56. 8000
57. 120
58. 800
59. 20 000
60. £40
61. 400 g
62. 21 074
63. 1100
64. £61.20
65. 300 ml
66. 110 hours
67. 3 × 940 = 2820
    940 + 2820 = 3760
    £3760 is more than
    their £3500 target.

Page 25: Short Multiplication

Set A

1. 2496
2. 6585
3. 13 004
4. 12 219
5. 19 284
6. 20 504
7. 21 305
8. 25 260
9. 35 210
10. £16 944

Set B

1. 32 310
2. 29 216
3. 33 276
4. 14 595
5. 26 365
6. 18 369
7. 39 214
8. 32 208
9. 21 595
10. 22 536
11. 9303

Set C

1. 42 365
2. 30 289
3. 73 648
4. 27 981
5. 25 560
6. 50 638
7. 30 044
8. 42 125
9. 20 811
10. 45 339 miles
11. 58 293 miles
12. 671 568

Page 26: Long Multiplication

Set A

1. 6095	**5.** 145 673	**9.** 17 472
2. 17 816	**6.** 108 250	**10.** 74 712
3. 14 883	**7.** 9744	**11.** 215 424
4. 49 566	**8.** 10 608	**12.** 143 605

Set B

1. 21 164	**5.** 153 846	**9.** 203 906
2. 27 435	**6.** 139 401	**10.** 124 176
3. 28 080	**7.** 39 744	**11.** 182 832
4. 102 088	**8.** 34 282	**12.** 168 475

Set C

1. 43 524	**6.** 20 119	**11.** 30 418 g
2. 394 524	**7.** 548 184	**12.** 41 768 g
3. 566 308	**8.** 421 770	**13.** 252 044
4. 8284	**9.** 371 424	**14.** 279 916
5. 67 704	**10.** 360 282	

Page 27: Short Division

Set A

1. 24	**5.** 31 r 7	**8.** 331 r 5
2. 13	**6.** 23 r 10	**9.** 3
3. 11	**7.** 603 r 2	**10.** 203
4. 12		

Set B

1. 21	**5.** 246 r 3	**8.** 132 r 6
2. 87	**6.** 165 r 8	**9.** 36
3. 43	**7.** 132 r 12	**10.** 690
4. 33		

Set C

1. 59	**5.** 359 r 10	**8.** 58 r 16
2. 654	**6.** 231 r 6	**9.** 178
3. 132	**7.** 274 r 7	**10.** 166
4. 363		

Page 28: Long Division — 1

Set A

1. 43	**6.** 27	**11.** 58
2. 74	**7.** 158	**12.** 59
3. 64	**8.** 596	**13.** 167
4. 49	**9.** 43	**14.** 634
5. 32	**10.** 36	

Set B

1. 67	**6.** 364	**11.** 452
2. 42	**7.** 159	**12.** 228
3. 41	**8.** 109	**13.** 342
4. 37	**9.** 29	**14.** 42
5. 583	**10.** 34	

Set C

1. 309	**6.** 294	**11.** £408
2. 159	**7.** 415	**12.** £357
3. 134	**8.** 316	**13.** £336
4. 573	**9.** 46	**14.** £204
5. 52	**10.** 26	**15.** £136

Page 29: Long Division — 2

Set A

1. 45 r 4	**8.** 173 r 3
2. 34 r 1	**9.** $81 \frac{6}{12}$ or $81 \frac{1}{2}$
3. 59 r 5	
4. 27 r 2	**10.** $36 \frac{1}{21}$
5. 48 r 4	
6. 66 r 1	**11.** $53 \frac{7}{14}$ or $53 \frac{1}{2}$
7. 141 r 3	**12.** 114

Set B

1. 68 r 2	
2. 33 r 4	**7.** $285 \frac{8}{16}$ or $285 \frac{1}{2}$
3. 57 r 2	
4. 113 r 6	**8.** $326 \frac{5}{23}$
5. $126 \frac{3}{21}$ or $126 \frac{1}{7}$	**9.** $32 \frac{2}{39}$
	10. 54
6. $151 \frac{1}{17}$	**11.** 72

Set C

1. 317 r 1	
2. 657 r 8	**7.** $386 \frac{5}{17}$
3. 61 r 2	
4. 284 r 9	**8.** $349 \frac{6}{27}$ or $349 \frac{2}{9}$
5. $515 \frac{6}{16}$ or $515 \frac{3}{8}$	**9.** $76 \frac{16}{35}$
	10. 72
6. $202 \frac{2}{19}$	**11.** 96

Page 30: Calculations — Review 3

1. 996
2. 9708
3. 18 030
4. 18 028
5. 37 478
6. 13 830
7. 18 939
8. 40 840
9. 17 230
10. 28 230
11. 31 656
12. 34 740
13. 7968
14. 14 240
15. 10 780
16. 337 466
17. 330 402
18. 740 265
19. 10 048
20. 23 670
21. 9144
22. 623 077
23. 410 592
24. 633 906
25. 32 835
26. £70 360
27. 130 060
28. 625 443
29. 57
30. 81
31. 65
32. 231
33. 42
34. 52
35. 84 r 3
36. 32 r 5
37. 29 r 6
38. 731 r 8
39. 143 r 1
40. 361 r 9
41. 67
42. 22
43. 42 r 1
44. 57
45. 124 r 2
46. 338 r 12
47. 54 r 11
48. $54\frac{2}{13}$
49. 39
50. $57\frac{8}{16}$
51. 711
52. $341\frac{2}{27}$
53. $63\frac{15}{41}$
54. 24 hours
55. 50
56. 57

Page 31: Common Factors

Set A

1. 54, 108, 63, 99 and 18
2. 63, 36, 120 and 15
3. 2, 3 or 6
4. 2, 4 or 8
5. 3 or 9
6. 2, 3 or 6
7. 2, 4 or 8
8. 7
9. 1, 2, 3 and 6
10. 1, 2 and 4
11. 1, 2, 4 and 8
12. 1, 2, 4 and 8
13. 2 and 5
14. 11

Set B

1. 5
2. 3, 4, 6 or 12
3. 5 or 10
4. 3, 7 or 21
5. 4, 7, 14, or 28
6. 4 or 8
7. 1, 3 and 9
8. 1, 2, 3 and 6
9. 1, 3, 7 and 21
10. 1, 13
11. 1, 2, 7 and 14
12. 12 or 36
13. 14 and 28,
    14 and 42,
    28 and 42

Set C

1. 1, 2, 4, 8
   and 16
2. 1, 2, 3, 6,
   9 and 18
3. 1, 3, 11 and 33
4. 1
5. 1, 3, 5 and 15
6. 1, 2, 4, 8 and 16
7. 9
8. 8
9. 11
10. 8
11. 36
12. 22
13. Any multiple of 17
    (e.g. 34) will share
    common factors 1 and 17.
14. 1, 5, 7

Page 32: Common Multiples

Set A

1. e.g. 6, 12
2. e.g. 10, 20
3. e.g. 35, 70
4. e.g. 12, 24
5. e.g. 24, 48
6. e.g. 60, 120
7. 36, 60, 12 and 24
8. 21, 63 and 42
9. 40 and 80
10. 24, 36 and 48
11. 18, 27, 36 and 45

Set B

1. 20, 40
2. 24, 36
3. 28
4. 24, 30, 36
5. 35
6. 36
7. 108, 36 and 72
8. 24, 96, 48 and 72
9. 9
10. 12
11. 70
12. 36
13. 15
14. 66

Set C

1. 77
2. 56, 64, 72 or 80
3. 60
4. 60 or 72
5. 56
6. 72
7. 21
8. 60
9. 24
10. 42
11. 70
12. 60
13. The lowest common
    multiple is the two primes
    multiplied together.

Page 33: BODMAS — 1

Set A

1. 4, 8
2. 7, 5
3. 7, 63
4. 20
5. 5
6. 48
7. 10
8. 18
9. 72
10. Kelly
11. Rav
12. Suyin

Set B

1. 8
2. 336
3. 4
4. 121
5. 5
6. 100
7. 20
8. 4
9. 96
10. 63
11. 32
12. 7
13. $75 \div (15 + 10)$
14. $(100 - 91) \times 300$

Set C

1. $(14 + 4) \times 4 = 72$
2. $72 \div (87 - 79) = 9$
3. $(64 - 9) \times 6 = 330$
4. $10 \times (15 - 10) = 50$
5. $(30 - 9) \times 4 = 84$
6. $50 \div (5 \times 5) = 2$
7. 9
8. 217
9. 9
10. 37
11. 144
12. 11
13. $48 \div 8 + 4 = 10$
14. $5 \times (7 + 5) = 60$
15. $84 - 7 \times 7 = 35$
16. $4 \times 16 \div 2 = 32$
17. $144 \div (84 \div 7) = 12$

Page 34: BODMAS — 2

Set A

1.	6	6.	60	11.	56
2.	7	7.	40	12.	19
3.	43	8.	15	13.	(6 + 12) ÷ 4
4.	8	9.	60	14.	£4.50
5.	29	10.	17		

Set B

1.	3	6.	6	11.	29
2.	13	7.	17	12.	2
3.	30	8.	56	13.	(39 ÷ 13) × 7
4.	11	9.	19	14.	£21
5.	50	10.	18		

Set C

1.	114	7.	3	
2.	8	8.	6 × (15 − 3) ÷ 9 = 8	
3.	20	9.	true	
4.	74	10.	false	
5.	67	11.	false	
6.	8	12.	true	

Page 35: Calculations — Review 4

1.	2, 3 or 6	38.	24
2.	2 or 4	39.	63
3.	3	40.	55
4.	2, 4 or 8	41.	36
5.	2, 4, 8 or 16	42.	24
6.	2, 4 or 8	43.	120
7.	2, 4 or 8	44.	7
8.	2, 11 or 22	45.	41
9.	1, 2, 7, 14	46.	240
10.	1, 2, 3, 4, 6, 8, 12 and 24	47.	88
11.	1 and 5	48.	96
12.	1, 2, 4 and 8	49.	80
13.	1, 2, 3, 4, 6, 8, 12 and 24	50.	7
14.	1, 2, 3 and 6	51.	941
15.	1, 3, 5, 15	52.	5
16.	1	53.	128
17.	20	54.	4
18.	11	55.	18
19.	28	56.	490
20.	24	57.	480
21.	3	58.	Julian
22.	32	59.	4
23.	6	60.	12
24.	45	61.	29
25.	e.g. 30, 60	62.	60
26.	e.g. 20, 40	63.	36
27.	e.g. 24, 48	64.	86
28.	e.g. 90, 180	65.	80
29.	e.g. 88, 176	66.	317
30.	e.g. 18, 36	67.	48
31.	e.g. 12, 24	68.	30
32.	e.g. 36, 72	69.	8
33.	12, 24, 36, 48	70.	39
34.	any seven of 27, 36, 45, 54, 63, 72, 81, 90, 99	71.	58
35.	30, 60, 90	72.	517
36.	48, 24, 72	73.	(700 − 7 × 38) ÷ 45 = 9 r 29 9 tulips
37.	56, 28, 84		

Page 36: Rounding Answers

Set A

1.	7300, 7000	4.	99 900, 100 000	8.	26 250
2.	2200, 2000	5.	6 343 200, 6 343 000	9.	11 100
3.	48 300, 48 000	6.	58 750	10.	96 800
		7.	800	11.	5 470 000
				12.	5 500 000
				13.	5 000 000

Set B

1.	43 580, 43 600	4.	46 920, 46 950	7.	1 180 840 miles, 1 180 840 miles, 1 180 850 miles, 1 180 000 miles
2.	320, 350	5.	8 211 700, 8 211 700	8.	9 660 000
3.	247 840, 247 850	6.	1 180 837 miles	9.	500 000

Set C

1.	214 360, 214 350	5.	429 480, 429 500	8.	1 016 000, 1 015 000, 1 000 000
2.	3 927 360, 3 927 350	6.	6 997 060, 6 997 050	9.	5 200 000, 5 500 000
3.	580, 600	7.	1 016 714		
4.	116 580, 116 550				

Pages 37-38: Checking Calculations

Set A

1.	52 000 + 65 000	10.	360
2.	3300 ÷ 10	11.	8 000 000
3.	24 000 + 650 000	12.	230 000
4.	2450 × 10	13.	1 030 000
5.	3 100 000 + 4 900 000	14.	56 000
6.	6400 ÷ 20	15.	5 500 000
7.	4500 × 20	16.	300
8.	7 000 000 − 2 100 000	17.	158 000
9.	*see below*	18.	1 510 000
		19.	1 505 512

9.

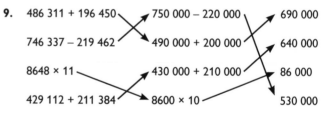

Set B

1.	5500 × 20	12.	168 000 and 158 650
2.	950 000 − 430 000	13.	700 000 and 707 110
3.	430 000 + 780 000	14.	228 000 and 213 220
4.	8000 ÷ 20	15.	100 000 and 102 832
5.	6 600 000 − 2 100 000	16.	840 and 761
6.	990 000 + 500 000	17.	30 000 and 31 887
7.	7600 × 10	18.	1 050 000 and 1 044 499
8.	6800 ÷ 20	19.	6 100 000
9.	690 000 + 270 000 = 960 000 440 000 − 210 000 = 230 000 330 000 + 590 000 = 920 000 940 000 − 130 000 = 810 000	20.	340
		21.	1 120 000
10.	687 000 + 272 000 = 959 000	22.	6 106 574 difference = 6574, 398 difference = 58, 1 113 079 difference = 6921
11.	958 880 The second estimation is more accurate.		

Set C

1. 740 000 − 310 000
2. 5700 × 20
3. 130 000 + 770 000
4. 7800 ÷ 10
5. 6 300 000 − 4 000 000
6. 5400 ÷ 20
7. 3100 × 20
8. 860 000 − 210 000
9. 8500 km
10. 46 500 km
11. 46 617 km
    difference = 117 km
12. 270 and 299
13. 6 500 000 and 6 537 564
14. 130 000 and 117 864
15. 1 050 000 and 1 049 013
16. 9 800 000 and 9 775 960
17. 475 and 498
18. 530 000 and 528 201
19. 1 970 000,
    400 000,
    7 810 000
20. 1 972 000,
    1 972 463
    The second estimation
    is more accurate.

Pages 39-40: Calculation Problems — 1

Set A

1. no
2. 450
3. 1 157 225
4. 42 m²
5. 72
6. 273

Set B

1. 634 337
2. 8 403 768
3. 1 865 506
4. 24 712
5. 141
6. 3 642 632 ₩
7. 38 488
8. 4655

Set C

1. 2277.68 kg
2. 1860.05 kg
3. £231 495
4. 61 362
5. 3 378 670
6. 11 933 040
7. 1 400 000
8. 108 cm or 1.08 m

Pages 41-42: Calculation Problems — 2

Set A

1. 753 282
2. 424 429
3. 3451
4. £27 608
5. 7971
6. 298
7. £71 489.55
8. 259

Set B

1. 131 908 m
2. 14 070
3. 1788
4. 44 415
5. 8800
6. £2464
7. £16 972.50
8. 53
9. 320 minutes or 5 hours
   20 minutes

Set C

1. 5390
2. 1 269 014
3. 413 690
4. £1 919 198
5. 3
6. £4149
7. 115

Page 43: Calculations — Review 5

1. 11 360, 11 400, 11 000
2. 87 700, 87 700, 88 000
3. 32 580, 32 600, 33 000
4. 650, 600, 1000
5. 393 220, 393 200, 393 000
6. 950, 1000, 1000
7. 900 180, 900 200, 900 000
8. 55 520, 55 500, 56 000
9. 717 640, 717 650
10. 960, 950
11. 55 820, 55 800
12. 454 220, 454 200
13. 540, 550
14. 1 293 680, 1 293 700
15. 4 192 820, 4 192 850
16. 7700, 7700
17. 1 520 000, 1 500 000
18. 5700 × 20
19. 53 000 + 18 000
20. 690 000 − 400 000
21. 9800 ÷ 10
22. 3 500 000 − 2 100 000
23. 280 000 + 310 000
24. 6400 ÷ 20
25. 3200 × 70
26. 150 000
27. 950 000
28. 225
29. 150 000
30. 1 460 000
31. 3 000 000
32. 150 000
33. 730
34. 840 000 and 839 009
35. 16 000 and 19 068
36. 360 and 398
37. 720 000 and 729 342
38. 10 100 000 and 10 003 675
39. 216 000 and 210 163
40. 2952
41. 175
42. 20 787
43. 5 290 391
44. 2718
45. 20
46. 11 596.51 km²
47. 68 364
48. 5

Pages 44-46: Calculations — Challenges

2. e.g. 75 − 63 ÷ 9 = 68
   e.g. 12 ÷ 3 × 11 + 239 = 283
   e.g. 15 × (14 − 3) = 165
   e.g. (16 + 4) × 5 × 10 = 1000
4. a) 6 004 999 m and 5 995 000 m
   b) 7499 m and 7475 m
   c) 7 449 999 and 7 350 000
5.

```
        7 ④
  ×    ⑧ 9
      6 6 6
    5 9 2 0
    6 5 8 6

      3 ⑨ 8 7
  ×      ⑤ 9
    2 3 9 2 2
  1 9 9 3 5 0
  2 2 3 2 7 2

    ① 8 ② 3
  ×      4 ①
    1 ⑧ 2 3
  7 ② 9 ② 0
  ⑦ 4 7 ④ ③
```

7. a) 24 × 4 = 96
   96 ÷ 6 = 16
   13 435 − 16 + 1107 = 14 526
   (14 526 − 9096) ÷ 30 = 181
   1600 × (181 + 76 ÷ 4) = 320 000
   b) £5 477 469
   c) £5 439 385

Section 3 — Fractions and Decimals

Page 47: Simplifying Fractions

Set A

1. $\frac{1}{2}$
2. $\frac{1}{3}$
3. $\frac{3}{4}$
4. $\frac{1}{2}$
5. $\frac{1}{4}$
6. $\frac{3}{4}$
7. $\frac{2}{3}$
8. $\frac{3}{4}, \frac{5}{8}, \frac{2}{7}$

Set B

1. $\frac{1}{3}$
2. $\frac{1}{4}$
3. $\frac{2}{5}$
4. $\frac{5}{6}$
5. $\frac{1}{4}$
6. $\frac{3}{5}$
7. $\frac{20}{30}$
8. $\frac{32}{40}, \frac{80}{100}$

Set C

1. $\frac{6}{8}$
2. $\frac{2}{3}$
3. $\frac{30}{54}$
4. $\frac{3}{5}$
5. $\frac{2}{3}$
6. $\frac{3}{11}$
7. $\frac{23}{40}$
8. $\frac{15}{20}$
9. $\frac{45}{75} = \frac{3}{5}$ and $\frac{120}{200} = \frac{3}{5}$, so $\frac{45}{75}$ and $\frac{120}{200}$ are equivalent.

Page 48: Ordering Fractions

Set A

1. $\frac{1}{2} = \frac{5}{10}$, $\frac{3}{5} = \frac{6}{10}$, so $\frac{3}{5}$ is larger.
2. $\frac{15}{20} = \frac{3}{4}$, $\frac{8}{16} = \frac{2}{4}$, so $\frac{15}{20}$ is larger.
3. $\frac{2}{7} = \frac{6}{21}$, $\frac{1}{3} = \frac{7}{21}$, so $\frac{1}{3}$ is larger.
4. $\frac{30}{36} = \frac{5}{6}$, $\frac{28}{42} = \frac{4}{6}$, so $\frac{30}{36}$ is larger.
5. $\frac{11}{10}$
6. $\frac{13}{8}$
7. $\frac{3}{2}$
8. $\frac{18}{15}$
9. $1\frac{1}{4}, \frac{7}{4}, \frac{11}{4}$
10. $\frac{7}{6}, 1\frac{2}{6}, 2\frac{1}{6}$
11. $\frac{4}{3}, 1\frac{2}{3}$, $2\frac{1}{3}, \frac{8}{3}$

Set B

1. $\frac{1}{4}$
2. $\frac{2}{3}$
3. $1\frac{5}{9}$
4. $2\frac{1}{12}$
5. $\frac{4}{11}$
6. $\frac{10}{6}$
7. $\frac{7}{4}$
8. $\frac{6}{5}$
9. $\frac{6}{4}, 2\frac{1}{2}, \frac{7}{2}$
10. $1\frac{3}{5}, \frac{11}{5},$ $\frac{24}{10}, 3\frac{1}{5}$
11. $\frac{11}{9}, 1\frac{5}{9},$ $1\frac{2}{3}, \frac{7}{3}$

Set C

1. $\frac{7}{30}$
2. $\frac{4}{5}$
3. $1\frac{1}{12}$
4. $4\frac{1}{5}$
5. $\frac{19}{8}$
6. True
7. True
8. Carlos
9. Felicia

Page 49: Adding Fractions — 1

Set A

1. $\frac{8}{10} = \frac{4}{5}$
2. $\frac{10}{24} = \frac{5}{12}$
3. $\frac{5}{15} = \frac{1}{3}$
4. $\frac{9}{12} = \frac{3}{4}$
5. $\frac{13}{6}$
6. $\frac{27}{8}$
7. $\frac{39}{20}$
8. $\frac{41}{16}$
9. $1\frac{2}{3}$
10. $1\frac{9}{10}$
11. $2\frac{7}{12}$
12. $2\frac{7}{16}$

Set B

1. $\frac{9}{16}$
2. $\frac{2}{5}$
3. $\frac{5}{8}$
4. $\frac{9}{25}$
5. $\frac{23}{14}$
6. $\frac{26}{15}$
7. $\frac{65}{22}$
8. $\frac{41}{25}$
9. $2\frac{7}{8}$
10. $1\frac{7}{18}$
11. $3\frac{2}{10}$ or $3\frac{1}{5}$
12. $4\frac{1}{9}$

Set C

1. $\frac{3}{4}$
2. $\frac{2}{3}$
3. $\frac{3}{4}$
4. $\frac{5}{6}$
5. $\frac{33}{20}$
6. $\frac{139}{16}$
7. $\frac{109}{50}$
8. $\frac{131}{32}$
9. $\frac{9}{4}$
10. $\frac{5}{3}$
11. $\frac{10}{21}$
12. $\frac{36}{30}$

Page 50: Adding Fractions — 2

Set A

1. $\frac{3}{6} + \frac{2}{6} = \frac{5}{6}$
2. $\frac{15}{20} + \frac{4}{20} = \frac{19}{20}$
3. $\frac{3}{30} + \frac{20}{30} = \frac{23}{30}$
4. $\frac{10}{45} + \frac{18}{45} = \frac{28}{45}$
5. $\frac{13}{12}$
6. $\frac{29}{24}$
7. $\frac{31}{18}$
8. $1\frac{31}{35}$
9. $\frac{11}{6}$ or $1\frac{5}{6}$
10. $\frac{13}{36}$
11. $\frac{17}{30}$
12. $\frac{7}{15}$

Set B

1. $\frac{7}{10}$
2. $\frac{5}{6}$
3. $\frac{17}{18}$
4. $\frac{14}{15}$
5. $\frac{29}{24}$
6. $\frac{47}{18}$
7. $\frac{149}{60}$
8. $\frac{53}{15}$
9. $1\frac{23}{40}$
10. $2\frac{3}{20}$
11. $3\frac{3}{22}$
12. $5\frac{1}{6}$

Set C

1. $\frac{16}{15}$ or $1\frac{1}{15}$
2. $\frac{4}{5}$
3. $\frac{9}{20}$
4. $\frac{19}{20}$
5. $\frac{101}{60}$
6. $\frac{329}{30}$
7. $\frac{121}{24}$
8. $\frac{429}{100}$
9. $\frac{2}{3}$
10. $\frac{3}{5}$
11. $\frac{5}{2}$
12. $\frac{11}{12}$

Page 51: Subtracting Fractions — 1

Set A

1. $\frac{2}{6} = \frac{1}{3}$
2. $\frac{2}{12} = \frac{1}{6}$
3. $\frac{21}{30} = \frac{7}{10}$
4. $\frac{2}{50} = \frac{1}{25}$
5. $\frac{9}{8}$
6. $\frac{13}{10}$
7. $\frac{10}{9}$
8. $\frac{25}{12}$
9. $1\frac{1}{10}$
10. $1\frac{1}{8}$
11. $2\frac{5}{9}$
12. $3\frac{9}{16}$

Set B

1. $\frac{3}{16}$
2. $\frac{1}{3}$
3. $\frac{5}{4}$ or $1\frac{1}{4}$
4. $\frac{13}{28}$
5. $\frac{11}{8}$
6. $\frac{31}{15}$
7. $\frac{43}{22}$
8. $\frac{35}{12}$
9. $3\frac{3}{16}$
10. $1\frac{17}{40}$
11. $1\frac{3}{4}$
12. $1\frac{7}{9}$

Set C

1. $\frac{1}{8}$
2. $\frac{1}{5}$
3. $\frac{1}{4}$
4. $\frac{5}{8}$
5. $\frac{16}{9}$
6. $\frac{29}{9}$
7. $\frac{58}{21}$
8. $\frac{43}{10}$
9. $\frac{5}{9}$
10. $\frac{5}{2}$
11. $\frac{13}{10}$
12. $\frac{51}{12}$

Page 53: Fractions and Decimals — Review 1

1. $\frac{1}{2}$
2. $\frac{3}{4}$
3. $\frac{1}{4}$
4. $\frac{1}{3}$
5. $\frac{2}{3}$
6. $\frac{6}{7}$
7. $\frac{2}{5}$
8. $\frac{5}{8}$
9. $\frac{1}{3}$
10. $\frac{2}{5}$
11. $\frac{3}{5}$
12. $\frac{1}{3}$
13. $\frac{3}{7}$
14. $\frac{14}{30}$
15. $\frac{13}{4}, 1\frac{1}{2}, \frac{5}{4}$
16. $\frac{17}{6}, \frac{8}{3}, 2\frac{1}{3}, 1\frac{1}{6}$
17. $3\frac{2}{3}, 2\frac{1}{5}, \frac{4}{3}, \frac{10}{9}$
18. $\frac{13}{8}$
19. $\frac{21}{10}$
20. $\frac{19}{12}$
21. $\frac{61}{16}$
22. $2\frac{3}{8}$
23. $2\frac{2}{9}$
24. $2\frac{5}{6}$
25. $4\frac{3}{4}$
26. $\frac{9}{10}$
27. $\frac{23}{30}$
28. $\frac{14}{15}$
29. $\frac{11}{60}$
30. $\frac{13}{20}$
31. $\frac{61}{110}$
32. $1\frac{5}{6}$
33. $2\frac{7}{20}$
34. $2\frac{7}{12}$
35. $2\frac{17}{66}$
36. $\frac{23}{10}$
37. $\frac{9}{8}$
38. $\frac{5}{3}$
39. $\frac{42}{25}$
40. $1\frac{1}{20}$
41. $4\frac{3}{4}$
42. $1\frac{7}{10}$
43. $2\frac{17}{20}$
44. $\frac{3}{10}$
45. $\frac{33}{50}$
46. $\frac{5}{24}$
47. $\frac{9}{20}$
48. $\frac{17}{60}$
49. $\frac{7}{110}$
50. $3\frac{1}{6}$
51. $1\frac{5}{12}$
52. $1\frac{17}{30}$
53. $3\frac{13}{30}$

Page 52: Subtracting Fractions — 2

Set A

1. $\frac{9}{12} - \frac{4}{12} = \frac{5}{12}$
2. $\frac{10}{15} - \frac{9}{15} = \frac{1}{15}$
3. $\frac{16}{30} - \frac{9}{30} = \frac{7}{30}$
4. $\frac{20}{28} - \frac{7}{28} = \frac{13}{28}$
5. $\frac{17}{6}$
6. $\frac{17}{12}$
7. $\frac{23}{15}$
8. $\frac{29}{30}$
9. $\frac{1}{10}$
10. $\frac{8}{21}$
11. $2\frac{7}{15}$
12. $1\frac{5}{12}$

Set B

1. $\frac{11}{24}$
2. $\frac{7}{44}$
3. $\frac{29}{60}$
4. $\frac{13}{20}$
5. $\frac{37}{18}$
6. $\frac{31}{22}$
7. $\frac{57}{40}$
8. $\frac{89}{60}$
9. $2\frac{7}{30}$
10. $1\frac{11}{30}$
11. $\frac{23}{24}$
12. $1\frac{9}{20}$

Set C

1. $\frac{2}{15}$
2. $\frac{3}{14}$
3. $\frac{1}{18}$
4. $\frac{13}{60}$
5. $\frac{47}{15}$
6. $\frac{25}{18}$
7. $\frac{79}{60}$
8. $\frac{79}{42}$
9. $\frac{5}{4}$
10. $\frac{14}{6}$
11. $\frac{11}{7}$
12. $\frac{5}{12}$

Page 54: Multiplying Fractions

Set A

1. $\frac{1}{6}$
2. $\frac{1}{30}$
3. $\frac{3}{20}$
4. $\frac{4}{15}$
5. $\frac{8}{21}$
6. $\frac{1}{3} \times \frac{2}{3} = \frac{2}{9}$
7. $\frac{1}{2} \times \frac{2}{5} = \frac{2}{10}$
8. $\frac{1}{2} \times \frac{1}{2} = \frac{1}{4}$
9. $\frac{1}{4} \times \frac{1}{3} = \frac{1}{12}$
10. $\frac{2}{3} \times \frac{1}{5} = \frac{2}{15}$

Set B

1. $\frac{1}{16}$
2. $\frac{3}{20}$
3. $\frac{5}{18}$
4. $\frac{21}{40}$
5. $\frac{8}{45}$
6. $\frac{2}{3} \times \frac{4}{5} = \frac{8}{15}$
7. $\frac{2}{5} \times \frac{5}{8} = \frac{10}{40} = \frac{1}{4}$
8. $\frac{1}{5}$
9. $\frac{1}{10}$
10. $\frac{1}{14}$
11. $\frac{9}{35}$

Set C

1. $\frac{1}{6}$
2. $\frac{1}{2}$
3. $\frac{4}{33}$
4. $\frac{5}{27}$
5. False
6. True
7. False
8. False
9. $\frac{1}{4}$ and $\frac{1}{6}$
10. $\frac{1}{4}$ and $\frac{2}{3}$

Page 55: Dividing Fractions

Set A

1. $\frac{1}{4}$
2. $\frac{1}{12}$
3. $\frac{1}{40}$
4. $\frac{7}{30}$
5. $\frac{4}{20}$ or $\frac{1}{5}$

6. $\frac{1}{7} \div 3 = \frac{1}{21}$
7. $\frac{3}{4} \div 2 = \frac{3}{8}$
8. False
9. True
10. True
11. False

Set B

1. $\frac{1}{36}$
2. $\frac{1}{80}$
3. $\frac{3}{20}$
4. $\frac{7}{24}$
5. $\frac{5}{45}$ or $\frac{1}{9}$

6. $\frac{1}{4} \div 2 = \frac{1}{8}$ or $\frac{1}{2} \div 4 = \frac{1}{8}$
7. $\frac{7}{8} \div 2 = \frac{7}{16}$ or $\frac{7}{2} \div 8 = \frac{7}{16}$
8. $\frac{1}{6}$ m
9. $\frac{1}{15}$ m

Set C

1. $\frac{1}{12}$
2. $\frac{1}{15}$
3. $\frac{1}{6}$
4. $\frac{3}{28}$

5. False
6. True
7. True
8. True
9. $\frac{2}{15}$

Page 56: Fractions of Amounts

Set A

1. 20
2. 36
3. 60
4. 25
5. 400

6. $\frac{1}{4}$ of 12 is equal to 3.

   $\frac{1}{2}$ of 8 is more than 3.

   $\frac{1}{4}$ of 4 is less than 3.
7. 42 g
8. 500 cm or 5 m

Set B

1. 30
2. 99
3. 300
4. 21
5. 90

6. 132
7. 120
8. 36 years old
9. He is correct because

   $\frac{2}{9}$ of 36 = 36 ÷ 9 × 2 = 8

Set C

1. 40
2. 72
3. 4
4. 24
5. 25

6. 1800 cm or 18 m
7. 4800 ml or 4.8 litres
8. 15 cm
9. 25 cm

Pages 57-58: Multiplying and Dividing by Powers of 10

Set A

1. Tens
2. Ones
3. Ones
4. Tenths
5. Hundredths
6. Tenths
7. × 10
8. ÷ 100
9. × 100

10. 460, 460
11. 4.4, 4.4
12. 52, 156
13. 750, 1500
14. 8, 0.08
15. 10.2
16. 30.007
17. 2.4

Set B

1. Hundreds
2. Tenths
3. Tens
4. Hundredths
5. Tenths
6. Thousandths
7. No — 0.375 × 10 = 3.75
8. 41.2, 82.4

9. 7.3, 21.9
10. 3105, 6210
11. 201, 20.1
12. 43, 0.43
13. 3002, 3.002
14. 10
15. 100

Set C

1. Tenths
2. Tens
3. Ones
4. Tenths
5. Thousandths
6. Hundredths
7. 300.5
8. 3945

9. 0.041
10. 76
11. ÷ 10, × 1000
12. ÷ 1000, × 10
13. 18 249 ÷ 1000

    18.249 × 100
14. 1824.9

Page 59: Fractions and Decimals — Review 2

1. $\frac{1}{12}$
2. $\frac{1}{40}$
3. $\frac{2}{21}$
4. $\frac{12}{25}$
5. $\frac{6}{55}$
6. $\frac{10}{27}$
7. $\frac{21}{80}$
8. $\frac{16}{63}$
9. $\frac{1}{8}$
10. $\frac{1}{18}$
11. $\frac{2}{20}$ or $\frac{1}{10}$
12. $\frac{21}{40}$
13. $\frac{6}{15}$ or $\frac{2}{5}$
14. $\frac{1}{6}$
15. $\frac{1}{30}$
16. $\frac{3}{40}$
17. $\frac{7}{24}$
18. $\frac{9}{50}$
19. $\frac{1}{72}$
20. $\frac{2}{10}$ or $\frac{1}{5}$
21. $\frac{11}{132}$ or $\frac{1}{12}$
22. $\frac{1}{8}$
23. $\frac{1}{50}$
24. $\frac{2}{9}$
25. $\frac{3}{40}$
26. $\frac{9}{99}$ or $\frac{1}{11}$
27. 18
28. 72
29. 160
30. 135
31. 92
32. 45
33. 42
34. 28
35. 24 cm
36. 125
37. Tenths
38. Tens
39. Tens
40. Tens
41. Hundredths
42. Thousandths
43. Tenths
44. Hundredths
45. 8060, 16 120
46. 104, 312
47. 49.2, 4.92
48. 2080, 20.8
49. £18 840
50. 0.15 m or 15 cm

Page 60: Multiplication with Decimals

Set A

1. 0.8
2. 1.8
3. 1.5
4. 7.2
5. 4.2
6. 5.5
7. 7.2
8. 268, 26.8
9. 804, 80.4
10. 56, 0.56
11. 657, 6.57
12. 2.1 litres
13. 8.4 litres
14. £12.80
15. £4.76

Set B

1. 5.6
2. 4.8
3. 72.9
4. 0.12
5. 0.81
6. 1.68
7. 8.48
8. 25.2
9. 35.45
10. 42.72
11. 159.42
12. 168.72
13. 1263.92
14. £24.96
15. 11.83 miles
16. 54.84 kg

Set C

1. 65.7
2. 1.26
3. 4.05
4. 25.76
5. 57.05
6. 57.08
7. 810.72
8. 67.2
9. 25.34
10. 36.6
11. 474.12
12. 612.34
13. 1706.85
14. 240.45 litres
15. £268.64
16. Yes —
   23 × 3.92
   = 90.16 m

Page 61: Division with Decimals — 1

Set A

1. 9.4
2. 16.5
3. 21.5
4. 6.5
5. 98.5
6. 106.5
7. 53.5
8. 164.25
9. 351.5
10. 86.4
11. 118.25
12. 85.5
13. 163.8
14. 47.5

Set B

1. 164.5
2. 117.6
3. 226.25
4. 94.75
5. 2.6
6. 3.4
7. 44.9
8. 22.25
9. 123.6
10. 28.75
11. 146.5
12. 82.25
13. 374.8
14. 404.5

Set C

1. 92.6
2. 45.25
3. 258.8
4. 513.25
5. 81.75
6. 26.88
7. 24.25
8. 240.25
9. 452.8
10. 183.6
11. £1719.75
12. 549.6 litres

Page 62: Division with Decimals — 2

Set A

1. 1.2
2. 0.6
3. 0.7
4. 1.2
5. 1.1
6. 1.1
7. 0.9
8. 9.7
9. 8.3
10. 10.2
11. 3.9
12. 10.9
13. 0.43
14. 0.83
15. 1.2 kg
16. 1.8 kg
17. 1.6 kg
18. 8.7 cm

Set B

1. 0.7
2. 2.4
3. 1.6
4. 0.09
5. 0.12
6. 0.17
7. 0.28
8. 0.65
9. 3.29
10. 1.55
11. 3.65
12. 2.54
13. 3.1
14. 0.98 m
15. 8.88 kg
16. £1.46

Set C

1. 0.24
2. 1.66
3. 7.14
4. 1.37
5. 1.85
6. 1.92
7. 5.35
8. 2.14
9. 3.13
10. 2.53
11. 3.35
12. 6.32
13. 3.34
14. £24.56
15. 2.45 g
16. 2.35 km

Page 63: Writing Fractions as Decimals

Set A

1. $\frac{8}{10} = 0.8$
2. $\frac{12}{100} = 0.12$
3. $\frac{15}{100} = 0.15$
4. $\frac{60}{100} = 0.6$

5. 0.2
6. 0.4
7. 0.28
8. 1.5
9. 5.25
10. 0.8 m
11. 0.333

Set B

1. $\frac{6}{10} = 0.6$
2. $\frac{36}{100} = 0.36$
3. $\frac{52}{100} = 0.52$
4. $\frac{240}{1000} = 0.24$

5. 0.85
6. 0.98
7. 2.64
8. 1.015
9. 0.375
10. 2.32 hours
11. 0.667

Set C

1. $\frac{8}{10} = 0.8$
2. $\frac{68}{100} = 0.68$
3. $\frac{16}{100} = 0.16$
4. $\frac{96}{1000} = 0.096$
5. 0.29

6. 0.758
7. 0.48
8. 3.95
9. 1.875
10. 0.111
11. 0.444
12. 0.475 m

Pages 64-65: Solving Problems with Decimals

Set A

1. 37 ml
2. 11 cm
3. 78.3 kg
   Check: 9 × 9 = 81
4. 196.6 m
5. 2.6 miles

6. £18
7. 29.6 litres
   Check: 4 × 8 = 32
8. 1.75 kg
9. 6
10. £93

Set B

1. 1.2 kg
2. £20.80
3. 2.7 km
4. 69.6 litres
5. 58.44 g
   Check: 10 × 6 = 60

6. £3.21
7. 12.46 m
   Check: 2 × 7 = 14
8. 4.32 m
9. 139 g

Set C

1. 1.8 kg
2. £45.99
   Check: 9 × 6 − 5
   = 54 − 5 = 49
3. 526 g
4. 20 ml
   Check: 80 − 9 × 7
   = 80 − 63 = 17

5. 2.16 m
6. £1094.25
7. 50.7 m
8. £3.96
9. 60 kg
10. 8.41 litres

Pages 66-67: Fraction, Decimal and Percentage Problems

Set A

1. 37%
2. 90%
3. 20%
4. 56%
5. see below
6. 90%

7. 0.65
8. 25%
9. 72%
10. 0.4 kg
11. $\frac{21}{50}$
12. 0.76 litres

5.

Fraction	Decimal	Percentage
$\frac{19}{50}$	0.38	38%
$\frac{4}{5}$	0.8	80%
$\frac{13}{50}$	0.26	26%

Set B

1. 36%
2. 35%
3. 84%
4. 62%
5. $\frac{1}{3}$
6. $\frac{7}{20}$

7. 28%, 0.25, $\frac{1}{5}$
8. $\frac{17}{20}$, 83%, 0.8
9. Olivia. $2\frac{2}{5} = 2.4$ m,
   which is further than 2.3 m.
10. $\frac{8}{25}$
11. 1.82 kg

Set C

1. see below
2. 0.434, $\frac{11}{25}$, 47%
3. 0.64, 65%, $\frac{2}{3}$
4. 1.509, $1\frac{27}{50}$,
   1.57, $1\frac{3}{5}$

5. 2.54, $2\frac{11}{20}$, 2.558, $2\frac{14}{25}$
6. $\frac{31}{50}$
7. 38%
8. $\frac{16}{25}$
9. 16.9 °C
10. 28%

1.

Fraction	Decimal	Percentage
$\frac{3}{20}$	0.15	15%
$\frac{6}{25}$	0.24	24%
$\frac{9}{20}$	0.45	45%
$\frac{14}{40}$	0.35	35%

Page 68: Fractions and Decimals — Review 3

1. 0.9
2. 0.35
3. 0.18
4. 4.8
5. 18.6
6. 16.2
7. 71.2
8. 30.66
9. 54.72
10. 39.65
11. 25.34
12. 35.04
13. 93.6
14. 17.36
15. 54.34
16. 274.4
17. 4.5 kg
18. 9.9 kg
19. £47.04
20. £94.08

21. 15.6
22. 23.5
23. 8.5
24. 36.4
25. 96.25
26. 1564.8
27. 227.25
28. 349.8
29. 140.6
30. 146.5
31. 86.25
32. 294.6
33. 289.75
34. 280.96
35. 1686.4 kg
36. 0.9
37. 1.2
38. 1.9
39. 0.07
40. 0.33

41. 0.21
42. 5.1
43. 0.89
44. 2.62
45. 3.88
46. 1.32
47. 2.62
48. 0.6
49. 0.68
50. 0.28
51. 2.96
52. 3.56
53. 0.875
54. 0.333 litres
55. 8.3 kg
56. 8.1 m
57. see below
58. $\frac{93}{100}$
59. 7%

57.

Fraction	Decimal	Percentage
$\frac{3}{5}$	0.6	60%
$\frac{42}{50}$	0.84	84%
$\frac{4}{25}$	0.16	16%

Pages 69-71: Fractions and Decimals — Challenges

1. a) 3500 kB
   b) 1.77 GB
   c) 20.055 MB

2. One third of the shape is made of 10 squares, so the whole shape has 3 × 10 = 30 squares. $\frac{1}{5}$ of 30 = 30 ÷ 5 = 6.
   So, Miro could be correct if one more square on the whole shape is shaded blue.

3. $\frac{3}{10} + 1\frac{1}{5} + \frac{17}{15} = \frac{9}{30} + \frac{36}{30} + \frac{34}{30}$
   $= \frac{79}{30} = 2\frac{19}{30}$
   $2\frac{19}{30}$ kg is less than 3 kg, so the conveyor belt is moving.

4. E.g. Damien is incorrect — $\frac{1}{2}$ can't be simplified.
   Tara is correct because you could always divide the numerator and denominator by 2.

5. a) E.g. $\frac{4}{6} \times \frac{1}{3} = \frac{2}{9}$
   b) E.g. $\frac{3}{6} \div 4 = \frac{1}{8}$

6.

	Fraction	Decimal	Percentage
Hurdle 1	$\frac{1}{10}$	0.1	10%
Hurdle 2	$\frac{1}{4}$	0.25	25%
Hurdle 3	$\frac{11}{20}$	0.55	55%
Hurdle 4	$\frac{9}{10}$	0.9	90%

7. a) $\frac{11}{12} = \frac{1}{2} + \frac{1}{3} + \frac{1}{12}$
   b) $\frac{3}{10} = \frac{1}{4} + \frac{1}{20}$

8. a) Small Box: £6.45 ÷ 3 = £2.15 per pumpkin basket.
   Large Box: £10.50 ÷ 5 = £2.10 per pumpkin basket.
   So the large box is better value.
   b) 6 small boxes
   (6 small boxes cost £38.70, 4 large boxes cost £42).
   c) He could buy 3 large boxes and 1 small box.
   This would cost him (£10.50 × 3) + £6.45 = £37.95.

Section 4 — Ratio and Proportion

Page 72: Scaling

Set A

1. 15 plums:

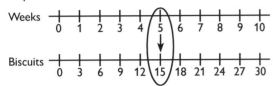

2. 9 months:

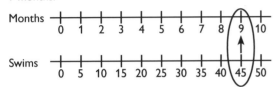

3. £400 ÷ 4 = £100
4. £100 × 5 = £500
5. £100 × 10 = £1000
6. 600 g
7. 1500 g
8. 2 litres

Set B

1. 300p or £3
2. 750p or £7.50
3. 8 litres
4. 48 litres
5. 1200 g or 1.2 kg
6. 125 g
7. 3200 g or 3.2 kg
8. 3
9. 4

Set C

1. 4 m²
2. £750
3. £1500
4. 300 km
5. 250 km
6. 150 ml
7. 3600 ml or 3.6 litres milk, 240 g cocoa powder

Page 73: Proportion

Set A

1. 2
2. 5
3. 6
4. 10
5. 15
6. 15
7. 9
8. 14
9. 20

Set B

1.

Brown	Grey	Total
1	4	5
4	16	20
10	40	50
20	80	100

2. 12
3. 18
4. 1600
5. 3
6. 30
7. 8
8. 2

Set C

1. 10
2. 100 ml
3. 70
4. 45
5. 30
6. 4
7. 1000
8. 4
9. 10

Page 74: Ratio

Set A

1. 3:4
2. 12
3. 1:2
4. 4
5. 16
6. 1:3
7. 18
8. 6

Set B

1. 2:5
2. 10
3. 10:3
4. 80
5. 45
6. 12
7. 30
8. 2

Set C

1. 45
2. 120
3. Yes, the ratio of rock CDs to pop CDs is 15:30. Divide both sides by 15 to give 1:2.
4. 1:1
5. 3:5
6. £4
7. 75
8. 80 litres

Pages 75-76: Sharing Problems

Set A

1. 5
2. 15
3. 8
4. 10
5. 4
6. 16
7. 10
8. Tom has 3, Luke has 18
9. Tom has 10, Luke has 60
10. 8
11. 20
12. 28
13. 12

Set B

1. 10
2. 50
3. 14
4. 36
5. 45
6. £18
7. £24
8. 20
9. 84
10. £80
11. 15 km
12. 8

Set C

1. 30
2. 15
3. 30
4. 56
5. 60
6. 720 ml
7. 600 ml
8. 162
9. 9 g
10. 8
11. 70
12. 75

Page 77: Ratio and Proportion — Review 1

1. 30 yoghurts:

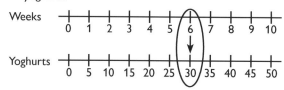

2. 32 miles:

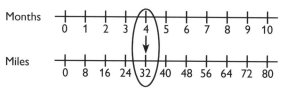

3. 4 days:

4. £30
5. £90
6. £150
7. £20
8. £120
9. 15
10. 240
11. 1600
12. 30 soft cheese, 10 blue cheese
13. 420 soft cheese, 140 blue cheese
14. £300
15. 35
16. 40
17. 5

18. 6:4 or 3:2
19. 20
20. 7:1
21. 5
22. 70
23. 140
24. 450
25. 15
26. 10
27. Stacey would have 50 and Liam would have 40
28. 54
29. Dougan ate 75 raisins, Kerry ate 225 raisins
30. Kerry paid £2.25 or 225p

Pages 78-79: Scale Factors

Set A

1.

2.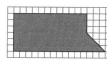

3.

4. 7
5. 10
6. 10 cm
7. 5 cm
8. 20 cm

Set B

1.

2.

3.

4.

5. 10 cm
6. 11 cm
7. 40 cm
8. 80 cm
9. 10
10. 7
11. 22
12. 15

Set C

1. 15
2. 18
3. 14
4. 17
5.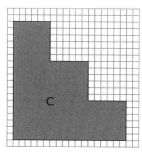

6.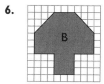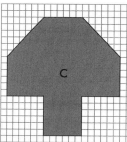

7.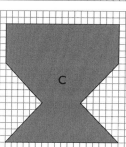

8.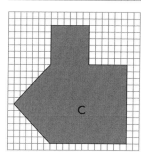

9. Yes. Every side is doubled so the perimeter is also doubled. 36 × 2 = 72

Page 80: Percentages of Amounts

Set A

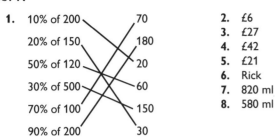

1. 10% of 200 → 20
   20% of 150 → 30
   50% of 120 → 60
   30% of 500 → 150
   70% of 100 → 70
   90% of 200 → 180

2. £6
3. £27
4. £42
5. £21
6. Rick
7. 820 ml
8. 580 ml

Set B

1. 40
2. 10
3. 80
4. 48
5. 165
6. 600
7. 20% of 150
8. 50% of 700
9. 1% of 300
10. 90% of 700
11. 25% of 700
12. Iain gets 1000 g, Ben gets 400 g, Kara gets 600 g
13. 72°

Set C

1. 715
2. 330
3. 50%
4. 80
5. £16.50
6. £8.40
7. £36

Page 81: Comparing Percentages

Set A

1. 40%
2. 30%
3. 40%
4. 70%
5. burgers
6. 40%
7. Hat

Set B

1. 10%
2. 75%
3. 36%
4. the bongo
5. Bag B
6. C
7. A

Set C

1. £3 off £20
2. £132 off £300
3. £350 off £500
4. £1350 off £1500
5. Renee
6. 14%
7. 56%
8. 6%

Page 82: Ratio and Proportion — Review 2

1.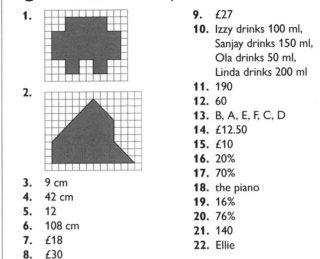

2.

3. 9 cm
4. 42 cm
5. 12
6. 108 cm
7. £18
8. £30
9. £27
10. Izzy drinks 100 ml, Sanjay drinks 150 ml, Ola drinks 50 ml, Linda drinks 200 ml
11. 190
12. 60
13. B, A, E, F, C, D
14. £12.50
15. £10
16. 20%
17. 70%
18. the piano
19. 16%
20. 76%
21. 140
22. Ellie

Pages 83-84: Ratio and Proportion — Challenges

1. a)
   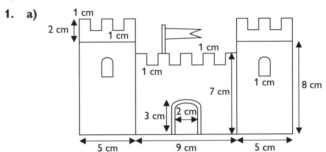

2. Yes. There are 6 marbles left, so if there are 2 red marbles and 4 blue marbles in the bag he is correct.
3. a) 20 000
   b) 15 000
   c) £50 000
4. Clarissa chooses B, D, H and L:
   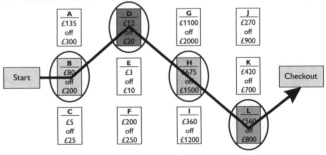

5. a) 75 ml
   b) Yes. E.g. There is 175 ml in the first flask and 300 ml in the second flask. As a ratio this is 175:300. Divide both sides by 25 to get 7:12.
6. Pirate 1 chooses cave 3 as it will give him 3 chests.
   Pirate 2 chooses cave 2 as it gives him 2 chests which is more than sharing the treasure in cave 3 with pirate 1 (1.5 chests).
   Pirate 3 chooses cave 3 as sharing 3 chests with pirate 1 will give them 3 ÷ 2 = 1.5 chests each, which is more than he'll get in either of the other caves.
   If pirate 4 chooses:
   cave 1, he will get 1 chest.
   cave 2, he will share with pirate 2 and get 2 ÷ 2 = 1 chest.
   cave 3, he will share with pirates 1 and 3, so he will get 3 ÷ 3 = 1 chest.
   So pirate 4 will get 1 chest whichever cave he chooses.

Section 5 — Algebra

Pages 85-86: Formulas — 1

Set A
1. 18
2. 36
3. 11
4. number of biscuits = number of cherries ÷ 5
5. 8
6. 30
7. £5
8. 4
9. cost of hall = £20 + (number of guests × £3)
10. 25 g
11. 10

Set B
1. 35
2. 9
3. number of carrots = 2 × number of peppers
4. 42
5. 22
6. amount Alice earns = £45 + (number of TVs × £5)
7. £70
8. 9
9. 60 g
10. amount of sugar = $\dfrac{2 \times \text{amount of butter}}{3}$
11. 40 g

Set C
1. 20
2. 95 minutes
3. £12.75
4. 3 miles
5. total cost = £25 + (number of matches × £1.50)
6. £38.50
7. 20
8. 100 ml
9. amount of white paint = $\dfrac{1}{3}$ × amount of red paint
   or
   amount of red paint = 3 × amount of white paint
10. 225 ml

Page 87: Formulas — 2

Set A
1. 48
2. 80
3. b = 10s
4. 28
5. 20
6. 54
7. L = 4D
8. 15 m
9. p = 4s
   (or p = s + s + s + s)

Set B
1. 15
2. p = 50c
3. p = 2w + 2h
   (or p = w + h + w + h,
   or similar)
4. 7 cm
5. £11
6. £41
7. 7

Set C
1. £22
2. 5 km
3. 4
4. p = 8a
5. q = nb
6. 120°
7. c (£) = 5 + 3p

Page 88: Sequences — 1

Set A
1. 17, 24, 31
2. 45, 34, 23
3. −2, 3, 8
4. 12, 18, 24, 30
5. 24, 21, 18, 15
6. 5, 3, 1, −1
7. −9, −5, −1, 3
8. add 4: 23, 27, 31
9. subtract 6: 11, 5, −1
10. add 3: 7, 10, 13
11. 30, 33
12. 60, 40

Set B
1. 28, 41, 54, 67, 80
2. 22, 11, 0, −11, −22
3. 4.5, 4.3, 4.1, 3.9, 3.7
4. 1, $1\frac{1}{3}$, $1\frac{2}{3}$, 2, $2\frac{1}{3}$
5. add 8: 41, 49, 57
6. add 7: 82, 89, 96
7. subtract 6: 57, 51, 45
8. subtract 9: −32, −41, −50
9. add $\frac{3}{7}$: $2\frac{3}{7}, 2\frac{6}{7}, 3\frac{2}{7}$
10. add 0.5: 3.4, 3.9, 4.4
11. 79, 72
12. 300, 750
13. $\frac{2}{5}$, 2
14. 40

Set C
1. 99, 80, 61, 42, 23
2. −30, −18, −6, 6, 18
3. $3\frac{1}{4}, 2\frac{3}{4}, 2\frac{1}{4}, 1\frac{3}{4}, 1\frac{1}{4}$
4. 7.7, 7.4, 7.1, 6.8, 6.5
5. add 11: 90, 101, 112
6. subtract 15: 105, 90, 75
7. add 0.4: −2, −1.6, −1.2
8. 92, 106
9. −25, 3
10. $3\frac{1}{2}, 3\frac{5}{6}$
    (accept equivalent fractions)
11. 22
12. 24
13. 51
14. 403

Page 89: Sequences — 2

Set A

1. 5
2. 7
3. 9
4. 11
5. 13
6. 23
7. 103
8. C
9. D
10. 5, 6, 7
11. 0, 1, 2
12. 4, 6, 8
13. 8, 11, 14
14. −1, 1, 3
15. 9, 13, 17

Set B

1. B
2. D
3. 6, 8, 10, 12
4. 0, 3, 6, 9
5. −5, −4, −3, −2
6. 8, 14, 20, 26
7. 8, 6, 4, 2
8. 60, 70, 80, 90
9. 3, 8, 13, 18
10. D
11. 48

Set C

1. 5, 8, 11, 14, 17
2. 3, 10, 17, 24, 31
3. −3, −1, 1, 3, 5
4. 1, −2, −5, −8, −11
5. 2, −2, −6, −10, −14
6. 15, 22, 29, 36, 43
7. C
8. 42
9. $2n + 9$: 11, 13, 15, 17
         add 2
   $5n + 3$: 8, 13, 18, 23
         add 5
   $9n − 1$: 8, 17, 26, 35
         add 9
10. The number you add to get from one term to the next is the number before n in the rule.

Pages 91-92: Missing Number Problems

Set A

1. 6
2. 4
3. 21
4. 9
5. 6
6. 12
7. 14
8. 8
9. 5
10. 20
11. 36
12. $\triangle − 7 = 9$
13. 16
14. $4\bullet = 20$
15. 5
16. 5
17. $4s = 24$
18. 6

Set B

1. 5
2. 9
3. 12
4. 12
5. 12
6. 4
7. 19
8. 2
9. $e = 3, f = 6$
10. 2
11. 1
12. 2
13. 4
14. 3
15. 2
16. $3\blacksquare − 2 = 16$
17. 6
18. $2r + 24 = 40$
   (or equivalent)
19. 8

Set C

1. 26
2. 6
3. 77
4. 3
5. 7
6. 2
7. 4
8. 27
9. 3
10. 9
11. $90 − 6b = 48$
12. 7
13. 2
14. $2p + 24 = 90$
   (or equivalent)
15. 33
16. $k + 44 = 3k + 30$
   (or equivalent)
17. 7

Page 90: Algebra — Review 1

1. 56
2. 4
3. sugar needed =
   (50 g × number of layers) + 20 g
4. 170 g
5. 7
6. 60
7. number of paint pots =
   15 × number of pupils
8. 300
9. 29
10. 10
11. $s = 150 + 45y$
12. 330
13. 9, 19, 29, 39
14. 220, 214, 208, 202
15. −1, −8, −15, −22
16. −6, −5.5, −5, −4.5
17. add 6
18. add 30
19. subtract 11
20. add 0.5
21. add 8
22. add $\frac{1}{10}$
23. 85, 75
24. $\frac{3}{4}$, $3\frac{3}{4}$
25. 7.2, 8.8
26. −6, 4
27. B
28. A
29. D
30. 11, 12, 13, 14
31. 10, 12, 14, 16
32. 2, 6, 10, 14
33. 14, 11, 8, 5
34. 40, 65, 90, 115
35. −1, −6, −11, −16
36. add 7

Pages 93-94: Two Missing Numbers

Set A

1. A, C
2. 6
3. 12
4. Any three of:

    ★ = 10, ▲ = 4

    ★ = 9, ▲ = 3

    ★ = 8, ▲ = 2

    ★ = 7, ▲ = 1

    ★ = 6, ▲ = 0
5. p + h = 10
6. Any two of:

    p = 1, h = 9

    p = 2, h = 8

    p = 3, h = 7

    p = 4, h = 6

    p = 5, h = 5

    p = 6, h = 4

    p = 7, h = 3

    p = 8, h = 2

    p = 9, h = 1
7. x = 1, y = 7

    x = 2, y = 6

    x = 3, y = 5

    x = 4, y = 4

    x = 5, y = 3

    x = 6, y = 2

    x = 7, y = 1

8. x = 1, y = 8

    x = 2, y = 7

    x = 3, y = 6

    x = 4, y = 5

    x = 5, y = 4

    x = 6, y = 3

    x = 7, y = 2

    x = 8, y = 1
9. x = 1, y = 16

    x = 2, y = 8

    x = 4, y = 4

    x = 8, y = 2

    x = 16, y = 1
10. x = 1, y = 20

    x = 2, y = 10

    x = 4, y = 5

    x = 5, y = 4

    x = 10, y = 2

    x = 20, y = 1
11. x = 1, y = 3

    x = 3, y = 2

    x = 5, y = 1
12. x = 1, y = 14

    x = 2, y = 10

    x = 3, y = 6

    x = 4, y = 2
13. B
14. b = 2r or $r = \frac{b}{2}$
15. b = 8, r = 4

    b = 6, r = 3

    b = 4, r = 2

    b = 2, r = 1

Set B

1. ⬡ = 1, ★ = 18

    ⬡ = 2, ★ = 9

    ⬡ = 3, ★ = 6

    ⬡ = 6, ★ = 3

    ⬡ = 9, ★ = 2

    ⬡ = 18, ★ = 1
2. ⬠ = 1, ● = 3

    ⬠ = 4, ● = 2

    ⬠ = 7, ● = 1
3. 6
4. c = 2, d = 4

    c = 3, d = 2
5. x = 1, y = 6

    x = 2, y = 5

    x = 3, y = 4

    x = 4, y = 3

    x = 5, y = 2

    x = 6, y = 1
6. x = 1, y = 30

    x = 2, y = 15

    x = 3, y = 10

    x = 5, y = 6

    x = 6, y = 5

    x = 10, y = 3

    x = 15, y = 2

    x = 30, y = 1

7. x = 1, y = 9

    x = 2, y = 7

    x = 3, y = 5

    x = 4, y = 3

    x = 5, y = 1
8. x = 1, y = 10

    x = 2, y = 8

    x = 3, y = 6

    x = 4, y = 4

    x = 5, y = 2
9. x = 2, y = 4

    x = 4, y = 3

    x = 6, y = 2

    x = 8, y = 1
10. x = 1, y = 5

    x = 2, y = 3

    x = 3, y = 1
11. f = 13, g = 1

    f = 16, g = 2

    f = 19, g = 3
12. B
13. c = 1, r = 19

    c = 2, r = 15

    c = 3, r = 11

    c = 4, r = 7

    c = 5, r = 3

Set C

1. ⬡ = 1, ● = 7

    ⬡ = 2, ● = 5

    ⬡ = 3, ● = 3

    ⬡ = 4, ● = 1
2. ⬡ = 1, ● = 6

    ⬡ = 2, ● = 3

    ⬡ = 3, ● = 2

    ⬡ = 6, ● = 1
3. ⬡ = 1, ● = 16

    ⬡ = 2, ● = 11

    ⬡ = 3, ● = 6

    ⬡ = 4, ● = 1
4. If c = 1, then 4d = 14. 14 ÷ 4 = 3.5, but d is a whole number, so this isn't a solution.
5. c = 2, d = 3

    c = 4, d = 2

    c = 6, d = 1

6. m = 20, y = 1

    m = 25, y = 6

    m = 50, y = 31

    m = 100, y = 81
7. x = 1, y = 19

    x = 2, y = 13

    x = 3, y = 7

    x = 4, y = 1
8. x = 1, y = 32

    x = 2, y = 16

    x = 4, y = 8

    x = 8, y = 4

    x = 16, y = 2

    x = 32, y = 1
9. x = 3, y = 2
10. x = 1, y = 20

    x = 2, y = 10

    x = 4, y = 5

    x = 5, y = 4

    x = 10, y = 2

    x = 20, y = 1
11. j = 5, k = 5
12. j = 2, k = 9

    j = 8, k = 1
13. 3c + 2p = 21
14. 3 cakes and 6 pies

Page 95: Algebra — Review 2

1. 14
2. 4
3. 17
4. 42
5. 12
6. 5
7. 8
8. 3
9. 7
10. 60
11. 6
12. 3
13. 10
14. 10
15. 4
16. 4
17. 8
18. $y + 47 = 180$
19. 133
20. $2z + 12 = 22$

21. 5

22. ⬟ = 1, ● = 4
   ⬟ = 2, ● = 3
   ⬟ = 3, ● = 2
   ⬟ = 4, ● = 1

23. ⬟ = 1, ● = 21
   ⬟ = 3, ● = 7
   ⬟ = 7, ● = 3
   ⬟ = 21, ● = 1

24. ⬟ = 1, ● = 20
   ⬟ = 2, ● = 15
   ⬟ = 3, ● = 10
   ⬟ = 4, ● = 5

25. D
26. $a = 8$, $b = 22$
   $a = 16$, $b = 14$
   $a = 24$, $b = 6$
27. $c = 2$, $d = 17$
   $c = 3$, $d = 13$
   $c = 5$, $d = 5$
28. $x = 1$, $y = 4$
   $x = 2$, $y = 3$
   $x = 3$, $y = 2$
   $x = 4$, $y = 1$
29. $x = 1$, $y = 26$
   $x = 2$, $y = 13$
   $x = 13$, $y = 2$
   $x = 26$, $y = 1$
30. $x = 1$, $y = 15$
   $x = 3$, $y = 5$
   $x = 5$, $y = 3$
   $x = 15$, $y = 1$
31. $x = 1$, $y = 4$
   $x = 3$, $y = 3$
   $x = 5$, $y = 2$
   $x = 7$, $y = 1$
32. $x = 2$, $y = 4$
   $x = 5$, $y = 3$
   $x = 8$, $y = 2$
   $x = 11$, $y = 1$
33. $x = 2$, $y = 6$
   $x = 5$, $y = 1$
34. $x = 1$, $y = 14$
   $x = 2$, $y = 7$
   $x = 7$, $y = 2$
   $x = 14$, $y = 1$
35. $x = 3$, $y = 3$
   $x = 6$, $y = 6$
   $x = 9$, $y = 7$
   $x = 18$, $y = 8$
36. $4t + 7m = 50$
37. $t = 2$, $m = 6$
   $t = 9$, $m = 2$

Pages 96-98: Algebra — Challenges

1. a) A: 7, 3, −1, −5, −9, −13
      B: 53, 50, 47, 44, 41, 38
      C: −10, −4, 2, 8, 14, 20
   b) A: −17, −21, −25
      B: 35, 32, 29
      C: 26, 32, 38
2. Graph A: $x \times y = 8$
   Graph B: $x + y = 8$
   Graph C: $x = 5 - y$
   Graph D: $x \times y = 4$
3. a) ANGLE
   b) Any equation where the solution is 12, e.g. ▲ − 8 = 4
4. a) D1
   b) A3
   c) C4
   d) A4
   e) Any formula in words that can be written as $H = 5 + F$.
      E.g. The number of hamburgers (H) that Una makes for a party is always 5 more than the number of friends she invites.
   f) Any formula in words that can be written as $T = P \times P \times P$.
      E.g. The total volume (T) of a cube with side length (P).
5. a) 2
6. a) Kamal bought 7 packets of peppers.
      Kamal bought 3 packets of potatoes.
      Kamal bought 3 packets of apples.
   b)

Potatoes	36	24	24	24	12	12	12	12	12
Apples	6	18	12	6	30	24	18	12	6
Peppers	6	6	12	18	6	12	18	24	30

   c) 12 potatoes, 18 apples, 18 peppers

Section 6 — Measurement

Page 99: Length — 1

Set A

1. 51 mm
2. 720 cm
3. 4600 m
4. 255 cm
5. 13.5 mm
6. 9050 m
7. 2.19 m
8. 1.38 cm
9. 9.14 m
10. 1.925 km
11. 1.693 cm
12. 2.275 km
13. 3.25 m
14. 3250 m
15. 325 m

Set B

1. 167 cm
2. 2.459 km
3. 1191 m
4. 30.52 mm
5. 5.258 m
6. 2.581 cm
7. 1.328 km
8. 753 cm
9. 3.91 mm
10. 1.068 cm
11. 58.59 mm
12. 4 m
13. 1.501 m
14. =
15. >
16. <
17. 13.2 cm
18. 0.132 m

Set C

1. 3.594 km
2. 7.29 mm
3. 1.514 cm
4. 31.96 mm
5. 4521 m
6. 970.2 cm
7. 1.839 m
8. 500 mm = 50 cm = 0.5 m
9. E.g. Yes, you get 0.5 m because there are 10 × 100 = 1000 mm in a metre, so to convert from mm to m you divide by 1000.
10. 79 m
11. 7900 cm
12. 50 mm
13. 0.006 km
14. 0.095 m

Page 100: Length — 2

Set A

1. 15 miles
2. 16, 16 km
3. 40, 40 miles
4. 25 miles
5. 55 miles
6. 500 miles
7. 160 km
8. 320 km
9. 20 miles
10. 30 miles
11. 56 km
12. 80 km
13. 45 miles
14. 96 km
15. 800 km

Set B

1. 20 miles
2. 35 miles
3. 400 miles
4. 40 km
5. 720 km
6. 1600 km
7. 55 miles
8. 650 km
9. 65 miles
10. 960 km
11. 1 mile
12. 2.4 km
13. 4 km
14. 3 miles

Set C

1. 25 miles
2. 104 km
3. 200 miles
4. 480 km
5. 560 miles
6. 544 km
7. 3 miles
8. 5.6 km
9. 4 miles
10. 7.2 km
11. 5.4 miles
12. 9.2 km
13. 32 km
14. 75 miles
15. 44 km

Page 101: Mass and Capacity

Set A

1. 1300 ml
2. 4700 ml
3. 5150 g
4. 6750 g
5. 3540 ml
6. 7250 g
7. 1.2 litres
8. 1.8 litres
9. 5.27 kg
10. 8.99 kg
11. 3.58 litres
12. 6.84 kg
13. 3298 ml
14. 6.185 kg

Set B

1. 3680 ml
2. 4.54 kg
3. 2050 g
4. 3540 ml
5. 5.87 litres
6. 6.68 kg
7. 280 g
8. 0.96 litres
9. 2 ml
10. 58 g
11. 3.525 kg
12. 0.625 kg
13. 0.095 litres
14. 2275 ml
15. 90 g
16. 800 ml
17. 0.65 kg
18. 45 g

Set C

1. 2.369 kg
2. 1285 g
3. 161 ml
4. 0.035 litres
5. 0.006 kg
6. 0.009 litres
7. 8605 g
8. 0.09 litres
9. 1350 g
10. 500 ml
11. 1958 ml
12. 5.7 kg
13. 0.4 litres
14. 4259 g
15. 1.593 litres
16. 15 620 g
17. 0.011 litres
18. 11 079 g
19. 7.157 kg

Page 102: Time

Set A

1. 38 days
2. 143 mins
3. 279 secs
4. 616 mins
5. 79 hrs
6. 770 days
7. 150 mins
8. 36 hrs
9. 195 secs
10. 140 secs
11. 285 mins
12. 60 mins = 3600 secs
13. 120 mins = 7200 secs
14. 24 hrs = 1440 mins

Set B

1. 200 mins
2. 130 secs
3. 26 days
4. 305 days
5. 63 hrs
6. 7 mins
7. 3 hrs
8. 5 days
9. 8 weeks
10. 2 days 12 hrs
11. 5 mins 30 secs
12. 3600 secs
13. 18 000 secs
14. 36 000 secs
15. 1440 mins
16. 7200 mins

Set C

1. 190 mins
2. 67 days
3. 134 hrs
4. 348 mins
5. 105 hrs
6. 9 weeks 5 days
7. 4 hrs 45 mins
8. 7 mins 15 secs
9. 5 days 14 hrs
10. 40 days 18 hrs
11. 23 mins 45 secs
12. 28 days = 672 hrs
13. 180 mins = 10 800 secs
14. 48 hrs = 2880 mins
15. 1680 hrs
16. 72 000 secs
17. 17 520 hrs

Pages 103-104: Solving Problems with Measure

Set A

1. 2300 g
2. 240 mins
3. 330 mins
4. 1800 g
5. 1157 g
6. 750 ml
7. 0.845 litres
8. 352 mm
9. 16.2 cm
10. 2 km
11. 1250 m
12. 19.75 km
13. 50 miles

Set B

1. 7800 ml
2. 10.3 litres
3. 40 km
4. 35 miles
5. 2 hrs 45 mins
6. 1200 secs
7. 85 mins
8. Speedy
9. 0.35 mm
10. 2.731 cm
11. 5111 m
12. 740 m
13. 4.626 km
14. 6.63 kg

Set C

1. 7.42 kg
2. 220 g
3. 7.35 kg
4. 370 g
5. 225 miles
6. 744 km
7. 4.75 m
8. 295.7 cm
9. 11873 ml
10. 11.218 litres
11. 11
12. 3180 mins
13. 37 hours

Page 105: Measurement — Review 1

1. 48 mm
2. 2700 m
3. 172.5 mm
4. 875 cm
5. 4380 m
6. 1525 m
7. 129.5 cm
8. 6.45 mm
9. 4.53 m
10. 3.55 km
11. 92.3 m
12. 2.052 cm
13. 0.756 m
14. 7.541 km
15. 0.062 km
16. 1.672 m
17. =
18. >
19. =
20. <
21. <
22. >
23. 10 miles
24. 15 miles
25. 35 miles
26. 250 miles
27. 300 miles
28. 550 miles
29. 32 km
30. 64 km
31. 96 km
32. 240 km
33. 320 km
34. 800 km
35. 2 miles
36. 5.6 km
37. 6 miles
38. 10 km
39. 14.32 km
40. 6.6 miles
41. 6400 ml
42. 8250 g
43. 2360 ml
44. 3755 g
45. 1.9 kg
46. 1.34 litres
47. 7.234 kg
48. 0.029 litres
49. 3.456 litres
50. 0.04 kg
51. 23.73 litres
52. 3.255 kg
53. 255 minutes
54. 320 seconds
55. 66 hours
56. 52 days
57. 281 seconds
58. 195 hours
59. 46 days
60. 12 weeks 6 days
61. 7 days 5 hours
62. 240 minutes = 14 400 seconds
63. 2880 minutes
64. 60 cm
65. 3 hours 35 minutes
66. 36

Pages 106-107: Area of a Triangle

Set A

1. 6 cm^2
2. 54 cm^2
3. 14 cm^2
4. 15 cm^2
5. 2 cm^2
6. 8 cm^2
7. 12 cm^2
8. 15 cm^2
9. B and C

Set B

1. 10 cm^2
2. 5 cm^2
3. 24 cm^2
4. 180 cm^2
5. 900 cm^2
6. 500 cm^2
7. 24.5 cm^2
8. 49.5 cm^2
9. 28 cm^2
10. 150 cm^2
11. 60.5 cm^2
12. 8 cm
13. A = 17.5 cm^2
    B = 12.5 cm^2
    C = 5 cm^2

Set C

1. 96 cm^2
2. 31.5 cm^2
3. 51 cm^2
4. 42.75 cm^2
5. A = 16 cm^2
   B = 28 cm^2
   C = 12 cm^2
   D = 16 cm^2
   E = 48 cm^2
   F = 32 cm^2

6.

Height	Base	Area
7 cm	12 cm	42 cm^2
8 cm	9 cm	36 cm^2
6 cm	4 cm	12 cm^2

7. 22 cm^2
8. 7 cm^2
9. 24 cm^2

Pages 108-109: Area of a Parallelogram

Set A

1. 15 cm²
2. 32 cm²
3. 77 cm²
4. 120 cm²
5. 108 cm²
6. 112 cm²
7. 450 cm²
8. 3600 cm²
9. A, C and D

Set B

1. 48 cm²
2. 132 cm²
3. 162 cm²
4. 1200 cm²
5. 22 cm²
6. 55.2 cm²
7. 25.6 cm²
8. 39 cm²

9.

Height	Base	Area
4 cm	7 cm	28 cm²
5 cm	13 cm	65 cm²
4.5 cm	8 cm	36 cm²

10. A = 3 cm
    B = 2 cm

Set C

1. 81 cm²
2. 51 cm²
3. 93.6 cm²
4. 67.9 cm²
5. 72 cm²
6. 42 cm²

7.

Height	Base	Area
6 cm	8 cm	48 cm²
6 cm	7 cm	42 cm²
9 cm	3 cm	27 cm²

8. 14 cm²
9. 64 cm²
10. 21 cm²

Pages 110-111: Perimeter and Area

Set A

1. C
2. A
3. B, A, C
4.

Width	Length	Perimeter	Area
1 cm	18 cm	38 cm	18 cm²
2 cm	9 cm	22 cm	18 cm²
3 cm	6 cm	18 cm	18 cm²

5.

6. Any rectangle with a perimeter of 18 cm. E.g.

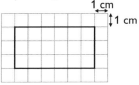

Area = 18 cm²

7.

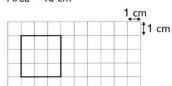

8. E.g.

Perimeter = 20 cm

Set B

1. 30 cm
2. E
3. D
4. B
5. A
6. E.g.

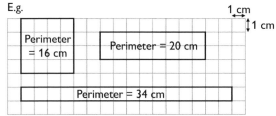

7.

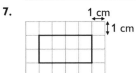

8.

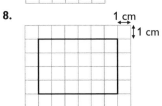

9.

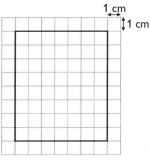

Width	Length	Area
2 cm	9 cm	18 cm²
4 cm	7 cm	28 cm²
5 cm	6 cm	30 cm²
3 cm	8 cm	24 cm²

Set C

1. 4 cm and 3 cm
2.

Width	Length	Area
1 cm	11 cm	11 cm²
2 cm	10 cm	20 cm²
3 cm	9 cm	27 cm²
5 cm	7 cm	35 cm²
4 cm	8 cm	32 cm²

3. smallest
4. 58 cm
5.

6.

7.

8.

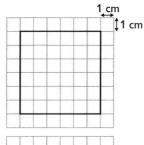

9.

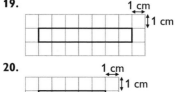

Page 112: Measurement — Review 2

1. 30 cm²
2. 14 cm²
3. 160 cm²
4. 31.5 cm²
5. B
6. 18 cm²
7. 42 cm²
8. A = 7.5 cm²
   B = 10 cm²
   C = 2.5 cm²
9. 42 cm²
10. 4800 cm²
11. 54 cm²
12. 144 cm²
13. 96 cm²
14. 5 cm
15. 21 cm²
16. C
17. B
18. B, C, A

19.

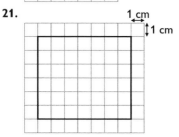

20.

21.

Pages 113-114: Calculating Volume

Set A

1. 8 cm³
2. 8 cm³
3. 18 cm³
4. 27 cm³
5. 3 × 2 × 2 = 12 cm³
6. 3 × 4 × 2 = 24 cm³
7. 4 × 4 × 1 = 16 cm³
8. 64 cm³
9. 30 cm³
10. 300 cm³
11. 144 cm³

Set B

1. 27 cm³
2. 80 cm³
3. 120 cm³
4. 112 m³
5. 36 cm³
6. 64 cm³
7. 24
8. 48
9. 3 cm
10. 28 cm³
11. 510 cm³

Set C

1. 144 cm³
2. 192 cm³
3. 80 cm³
4. 142.5 cm³
5. 80 cm³
6. 100 cm³
7. 4 cm

8.

Length	Width	Height	Volume
5 m	4 m	3 m	60 m³
3 mm	2 mm	1 mm	6 mm³
2 cm	6 cm	7 cm	84 cm³
8 cm	3 cm	2 cm	48 cm³

9. 16 cm³
10. 192 cm³

Pages 115-116: Comparing Volume

Set A

1. A
2. D
3. 18 cm³
4. 8 cm³
5. 12 cm³
6. F and H
7. G
8. E
9. 69 m³

Set B

1. B
2. E
3. C
4. 6 cm³
5. H
6. 120 cm³
7. J
8. 6 m³

Set C

1. B
2. 8 cm³
3. D
4. 40 mm³
5. *Any 3 of:*
   1 cm, 1 cm, 36 cm
   1 cm, 2 cm, 18 cm
   1 cm, 4 cm, 9 cm
   1 cm, 6 cm, 6 cm
   2 cm, 2 cm and 9 cm
   2 cm, 3 cm and 6 cm
   3 cm, 3 cm and 4 cm
6. 8 cm
7. 25 cm

Page 117: Measurement — Review 3

1. 36 cm^3
2. 60 cm^3
3. 72 cm^3
4. 20 cm^3
5. 270 cm^3
6. 90 cm^3
7. 3 cm
8. 8 cm
9. 16 cm^3
10. 24 cm^3
11. C
12. A
13. A and D
14. 3
15. G
16. 24 cm^3
17. 8 cm

Pages 118-119: Measurement — Challenges

1. **a)** Work out the area of the rectangle:
    $10 \times 8 = 80 \text{ m}^2$
    Then work out the area of each brown triangle:
    $\frac{1}{2} \times 10 \times 3 = 15 \text{ m}^2$
    $\frac{1}{2} \times 6 \times 5 = 15 \text{ m}^2$
    $\frac{1}{2} \times 4 \times 8 = 16 \text{ m}^2$
    Subtract the area of the brown triangles from the area of the rectangle:
    $80 - 15 - 15 - 16 = 34 \text{ m}^2$

    Work out the area of the parallelogram:
    $11 \times 7 = 77 \text{ m}^2$
    Then work out the area of each brown triangle:
    $\frac{1}{2} \times 11 \times 7 = 38.5 \text{ m}^2$
    $\frac{1}{2} \times 11 \times 2 = 11 \text{ m}^2$
    Subtract the area of the brown triangles from the area of the parallelogram:
    $77 - 38.5 - 11 = 27.5 \text{ m}^2$

    b) $17 + 13 = 30$
2. **a)** 11.5 hours
    b) 11 pm or 23:00 on 2nd January
    c) 12:35 am or 00:35
    d) Mumbai
    e) 1:45 pm or 13:45
3. **a)** Greyville
    b) **(i)** Greyville and Gleastown
        or Jollysthorpe, Southbeach and Eastville
        (ii) Haysea, Jollysthorpe, Gleastown, Floraby = 50 miles
    c) He could be in:
        Jollysthorpe, Greyville, Lunaland, Eastville or Floraby
    d) Jollysthorpe and Haysea
4. **a)** 432 (You could get 18 small boxes in a large box.)
    b) Increase 0.35 m by 1 cm to 0.36 m.
        Increase both 0.45 m sides by 3 cm to 0.48 m.
    c) 1152

Section 7 — Geometry

Pages 120-121: Angles in Shapes — 1

Set A

1. 120°
   120°, 60°
2. 150°
   150°, 30°
3. 135°
   135°, 45°

4. 60°
5. 100°
6. 50°
7. 75°

8. 65°
   65°
   130°
   130°, 50°

Set B

1. 85°
2. 78°
3. 52°
4. 38°

5. 109°
6. 52°
7. 55°
8. 42°

9. p = 30°, q = 120°
10. r = 81°, s = 18°
11. t = 35°, u = 35°
12. v = 76°, w = 76°

Set C

1. 111°
2. 39°
3. c = 77°, d = 26°
4. e = 71°, f = 71°

5. g = 112°
6. h = 44°
7. 54°, isosceles
8. 85°, scalene

9. 60°, equilateral
10. 39°, isosceles
11. B, D, E

Pages 122-123: Angles in Shapes — 2

Set A

1. 290°
   290°, 70°
2. 240°
   240°, 120°
3. 245°
   245°, 115°

4. d = 115°
5. e = 145°
6. f = 50°
7. g = 115°

8. 110°
   110°
   300°
   300°, 60°

Set B

1. a = 105°
2. b = 133°
3. c = 99°
4. d = 80°

5. e = 101°,
   f = 91°
6. g = 56°,
   h = 138°
7. i = 120°,
   j = 120°
8. k = 59°,
   l = 59°

9. m = 115°,
   n = 115°
10. p = 59°,
    q = 59°
11. r = 107°, s = 73°,
    t = 73°
12. u = 54°, v = 126°,
    w = 126°

Set C

1. a = 56°
2. b = 117°
3. c = 101°,
   d = 101°
4. e = 69°,
   f = 111°,
   g = 111°
5. h = 63°
6. i = 89°

7.
Kite	64° 107° 116° 73°
Rhombus	90° 109° 109° 52°
Trapezium	65° 115° 115° 65°

8. A, B, D

Page 124: Angles in Shapes — 3

Set A

1. a = 108°
   b = 108°
2. c = 135°
   d = 135°

3. 4, 360°
4. 6, 720°
5. 120°
6. 90°

7. 72°
8. 60°
9. 45°
10. 36°

Set B

1. a = 120°
   b = 60°
2. c = 140°
   d = 40°
3. 3
   1, 180°
4. 6
   4, 720°

5. 7
   5, 900°
6. true — exterior angles for all
   polygons add up to 360°
7. false — they add up to
   (5 − 2) × 180° = 540°
8. true — 360° ÷ 10 = 36°

Set C

1. a = 120°
   b = 60°
   c = 30°
2. d = 72°
   e = 36°

3. 4 sides
4. 6 sides
5. 10 sides
6. 20 sides
7. 30 sides

8. 60 sides
9. 360°
10. 900°
11. 1260°
12. 1800°

Pages 125-126: Angle Rules

Set A

1. 40°
2. 102°
3. 162°
4. 248°
5. 289°
6. 70°

7. 42°
8. 130°
9. 160°
10. 256°
11. k = 62°
    l = 118°

12. m = 147°
    n = 43°
13. 62°
    62° = 118°
    q = 62°
    r = 118°

Set B

1. a = 47°
2. b = 106°
3. c = 18°
4. d = 155°
5. e = 52°
   f = 128°
6. g = 80°
   h = 39°
   i = 61°

7. j = 37°
   k = 37°
8. l = 96°
   m = 84°
   n = 84°
9. p = 62°
   q = 62°

10. r = 64°
    s = 116°
11. t = 137°
12. u = 65°
    v = 115°

Set C

1. a = 36°
2. b = 37°
3. c = 56°
   d = 56°
   e = 124°
4. f = 33°
   g = 103°
   h = 33°
   i = 44°

5. j = 60°
   k = 120°
6. m = 63°
   n = 117°
7. p = 70°
   q = 70°
8. r = 63°
   s = 117°

9. x = 29°
   y = 61°
10. 30°
11. 210°
12. 135°
13. 108°

Page 127: Geometry — Review 1

1. a = 70°
2. b = 110°
3. c = 32°
4. d = 29°
5. e = 70°
   f = 40°
6. g = 63°
   h = 63°
7. i = 120°
8. j = 60°
9. k = 80°
10. m = 243°
11. p = 115°
    q = 75°
12. r = 75°
    s = 75°
13. t = 67°
    u = 67°
14. v = 64°
    w = 116°
    x = 116°

15.

Regular Shape	Exterior angle	Interior angle
Square	90°	90°
Hexagon	60°	120°
Nonagon	40°	140°
Decagon	36°	144°

16. 540°
17. 1080°
18. a = 46°
19. b = 57°
20. c = 71°
    d = 109°
21. e = 127°
    f = 53°
    g = 53°
22. x = 48°
23. 60°
24. 195°

Pages 128-129: Drawing Triangles

Set A

1-9. See diagrams 1-9 on page.

Set B

Note: for Qs 1-6, allow answers which are 5 mm or 3° either side of the given answers.

1. x = 64 mm
2. x = 32 mm
3. x = 32°
4. x = 83°
5. x = 99 mm
6. x = 26 mm
7.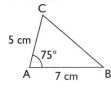

8.
9.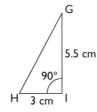
10.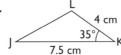

Set C

Note: for Qs 1-3, allow answers which are 5 mm or 3° either side of the given answers.

1. x = 40 mm
2. x = 26°
3. x = 39 mm
4.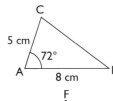
5.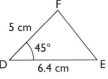

6.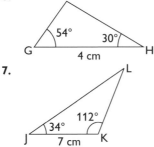
7.

8-9. See diagrams 8-9 on page.

Pages 130-131: Drawing Quadrilaterals

Set A

1-9. See diagrams 1-9 on page.

Set B

1. Square
2. Rectangle
3. Trapezium
4. Rhombus
5. Kite
6. Parallelogram

Note: for Qs 7-9, allow answers which are 5 mm or 3° either side of the given answers.

7. 57 mm
8. 128°
9. 64°

Set C

Note: for Qs 1-6, allow answers which are 5 mm or 3° either side of the given answers.

1. x = 53°
2. x = 104°
3. x = 85°
4. x = 66 mm
5. x = 72 mm
6. x = 20 mm
7.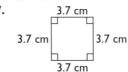
8.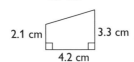

9.
10.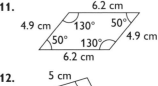
11.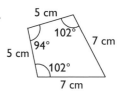
12.

Pages 132-133: Drawing Other Shapes

Set A

1-6. See diagrams 1-6 on page.

Set B

Note: for Qs 4-6, allow answers which are 5 mm or 3° either side of the given answers.

1. Pentagon
2. Hexagon
3. Quadrilateral
4. x = 59 mm
5. x = 27 mm
6. x = 135°

Set C

Note: for Qs 1-6, allow answers which are 5 mm or 3° either side of the given answers.

1. a = 55°
2. b = 115°
3. c = 43 mm
4. d = 53°
5. e = 74°
6. f = 20 mm

7.
8.
9.

Page 134: Geometry — Review 2

Note: for Qs 5-8 and 13-16, allow answers which are 5 mm or 3° either side of the given answers.

1-4. See diagrams 1-4 on page.
5. a = 31°
6. b = 52°
7. c = 75 mm
8. d = 51 mm
9.

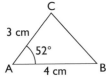

10.

11-12. See diagrams 11-12 on page.
13. a = 30 mm
14. b = 45 mm
15. c = 118°
16. d = 40°
17.

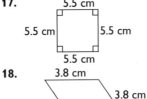

18.

5.5 cm
5.5 cm   5.5 cm
5.5 cm

3.8 cm
3.8 cm   125°   3.8 cm
          55°
      3.8 cm

19-21. See diagrams 19-21 on page.

Set C

1.

	Pairs of parallel sides	Lines of symmetry	Number of obtuse angles
Equilateral triangle	0	3	0
Rectangle	2	2	0
Regular octagon	4	8	8
Rhombus	2	2	2

2. square, rhombus
3. parallelogram
4. kite
5. square, rectangle
6. similarities: e.g. both have 6 sides, 6 angles, 1 line of symmetry, 2 acute angles, rotational symmetry of order 1
differences: e.g. left has right angles, left has parallel sides, right has obtuse angles
7. isosceles, 2 angles equal
8. scalene, all sides different
9. equilateral, all sides and angles equal
10. false — e.g. diagonals in a rectangle don't cross at right angles
11. true — e.g. regular heptagons have no pairs of parallel sides
12. false — e.g. a rhombus has equal sides but 2 pairs of equal angles

Pages 135-136: 2D Shapes

Set A

1. 3 sides,
3 lines of symmetry,
3 acute angles
2. 6 sides,
6 lines of symmetry,
no acute angles
3. C
4. D
5. B
6. A
7. P
8. P, Q
9. R, S, T
10. P, R, T
11. Q, R
12. the number of equal sides of a regular octagon
13. the number of lines of symmetry in an isosceles triangle
14. the number of lines of symmetry in a regular hexagon

Set B

1. heptagon,
0 pairs of parallel sides,
7 lines of symmetry
2. decagon,
5 pairs of parallel sides,
10 lines of symmetry
3. A, B
4. C, D, G, H
5. C, G, H
6. E, F
7. equilateral, all sides equal
8. isosceles, 2 angles equal
9. scalene, all angles different
10. isosceles, 2 sides same
11. false
12. false
13. true
14. true
15. false

Pages 137-138: Circles

Set A

1. a: circumference
b: diameter
c: radius
2. diameter: 2 cm
radius: 1 cm
3. diameter: 4 cm
radius: 2 cm
4. 6 cm
5. 14 cm
6. 20 m
7. 4 cm
8. 7 cm
9. 15 m
10. 12 m
11. 40 cm
12. 9 mm

Set B

1. 2 cm
2. 7 cm
3. 38 cm
4. 62 m
5. 23 cm
6. 37 m
7. false
8. false
9. true
10. false
11. 28 cm
12. 36 cm
13. 12 cm

Set C

1.

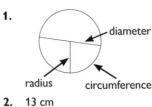

2. 13 cm
3. 34.6 m
4. 83.8 cm
5. 9.5 cm
6. 16.3 cm
7. 27.6 m
8. 30 cm
9. 1.5 m
10. 12.6 cm
11. 6 cm

Page 139: 3D Shapes

Set A

1. A
2. A
3. A
4. C, B, A
5. C, B, A
6. cube
7. triangular prism
8. tetrahedron

Set B

1. cuboid
2. triangular prism
3. sphere
4. A
5. D
6. C
7. 6
8. 5
9. 4

Set C

1. hexagonal prism
2. cube
3. square based pyramid
4. cylinder
5. hemisphere, tetrahedron, triangular prism, cuboid
6. tetrahedron
7. cuboid, triangular prism
8. false — both shapes have one circular face
9. false — a hexagonal prism has 12 vertices, and a cuboid has 8 vertices
10. true — octagonal prisms have 24 edges, and triangular prism have 9 edges

Pages 140-141: Making 3D Shapes

Set A

1. C
2. cube
3. tetrahedron
4. square based pyramid
5. triangular prism
6.
7.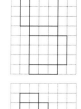
8.
9.
10.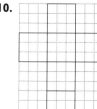
11.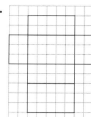

Set B

1. A, D
2. E.g.

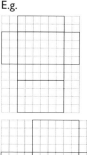

there are lots of other possible nets

3.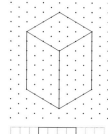

4.

5.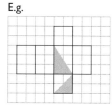

6.

7. E.g.

Set C

1. B
2. C
3.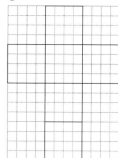

4.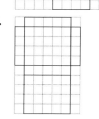

5.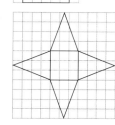

6.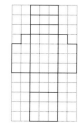

7.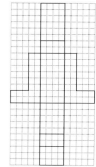

8. He has drawn two of the edges (the 3 cm and 4 cm edges) the wrong way round, and labelled the sides incorrectly.

9. E.g.

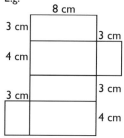

Page 142: Geometry — Review 3

1. 5, 5, 0
2. 4, 1, 1
3. A, B, C, D, E
4. B, F
5. A, C, E
6. D, E
7. equilateral — all of the angles are equal
8. scalene — all of the angles are different
9. isosceles — two of the sides are the same length
10. 18 cm
11. 80 cm
12. 15 m
13. 15 m
14. 4.5 cm
15. 11.5 m
16. C
17. B
18. C
19. D
20. false — a tetrahedron and a square-based pyramid both have 4 triangular faces
21. false — a hexagonal prism has 12 vertices, and a cube has 8 vertices
22. true — an octagonal prism has 24 edges, and a cuboid has 12 edges
23. cuboid
24. pentagonal prism
25.

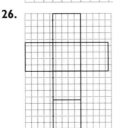

26.

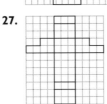

27.

Pages 143-144: Coordinates — 1

Set A

1. C
2. D
3. A
4. B
5. B
6. D
7. C
8. A
9. −4
10. 2
11. −3
12. 1
13. −4
14. −3
15. B
16. C
17. 2
18. −2
19. 2, −2
20. 2, −4

Set B

1. 1
2. −3
3. 0
4. −3, −2
5. H
6. E
7. (−5, 3)
8. (−2, 5)
9. F, G, H, J K, L, R
10. D, I, J, K, L, M, P
11. G, K
12. J, L, M
13. I, R
14. (3, −5)
15. (0, 5)
16. (−4, −1)

Set C

1. −6, 1
2. −5, 4
3. −3, 4
4. −2, 1
5. D
6. F
7. B
8. C
9. D
10. (0, 3), (2, 3), (3, 1), (2, −1), (0, −1), (−1, 1)
11. (2, −5)
12. (−4, 3)
13. (0, −2)
14. (−4, −1)
15. (−1, 4)

Pages 145-146: Coordinates — 2

Set A

1-6.

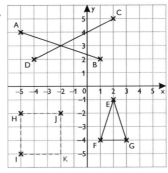

7. (−2, 3)
8. see diagram for Q1-6 to the left
9. isosceles
10. see diagram for Q1-6 to the left
11. (−2, −5)
12. (1, 1)
13. (8, 4)
14. (−1, 1) (1, 7)

Set B

1.

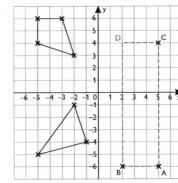

2. kite
3. see diagram for Q1 to the left
4. scalene
5. see diagram for Q1 to the left
6. (2, 4)
7. (−3, 2)
8. (2, −7)
9. (−3, −6)

Set C

1.

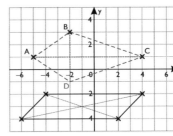

2. parallelogram
3. (−1, −3)
4. see diagram for Q1 to the left
5. (−2, −1)
6. (−2, 1)
7. (7, 0)
8. (−4, −6)
9. (10, 8)
10. (10, 4)
11. (5, −4)
12. (10, −8)
13. (−5, 4)
14. (−4, −5)

Pages 147-148: Reflection

Set A

1.
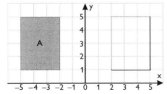

2.
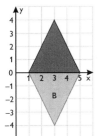

3.
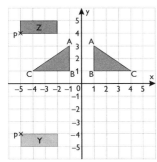

4. (−5, 4)

5-6. see diagram for Q3 above

7. A (−1, 3), B (−1, 1), C (−4, 1)

Set B

1-3.
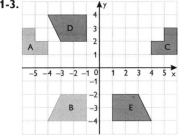

4. (−4, 4), (−1, 4), (−1, 2), (−3, 2)

5. (1, −2), (3, −2), (4, −4), (1, −4)

6-7.
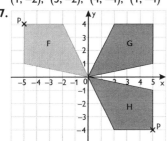

8. (5, −4)

9.
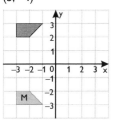

Set C

1-2.
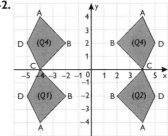

3. (2, −2) — e.g. the coordinates are the same, except that the x-coordinate has gone from negative to positive.

4. see diagram for Q1-2 above

5. (−2, 2), (2, 2) — e.g. the coordinates are the same except for the minus signs.

6-7.
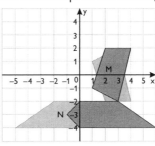

8-9.
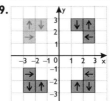

Pages 149-150: Translation

Set A

1. 7, 2

2. 8, 3

3. 8, 3

4. right, down

5-7.
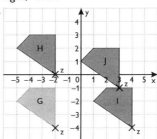

8. (−2, 0)

9. (3, −1)

Set B

1-2.

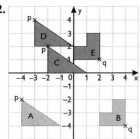

3. (–2, 2)
4. (–3, 4)
5. *see diagram for Q1-2 above*
6. (2, 1)
7. E.g. 6 units right
8. E.g. 5 units right and 1 unit up
9. E.g. 2 units left and 4 units up
10. (1, –4)

Set C

1-2.

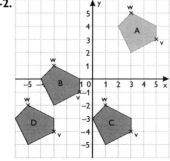

3. E.g. –2 units horizontally and –7 units vertically
4. (–3, 1)
5. (3, –4)
6. *see diagram for Q1-2 above*
7. E.g. –8 units horizontally and –7 units vertically
8. (–3, 0)
9. E.g. –7 units horizontally and +8 units vertically
10. E.g. –13 units horizontally and +10 units vertically
11. (8, 1)

1. (–3, 2)
2. (5, 3)
3. (–3, –4)
4. (–4, 5), (–2, 5), (–3, 4), (–5, 4)
5. C
6. O
7. R
8. N
9. P and H
10. S and N
11.

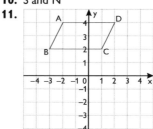

12. parallelogram
13. (7, –9)
14-16.

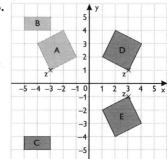

17. (3, 1)
18. (3, –1)
19. E.g. 6 units right and 1 unit up
20.

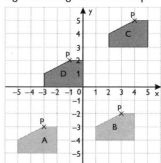

21. (4, 5)
22. *see diagram above*
23. E.g. 4 units right and 4 units up
24. E.g. 13 units right and 12 units down

Pages 152-154: Geometry — Challenges

1. a) B
b) D

2. a) square-based pyramid, tetrahedron, triangular prism

b)

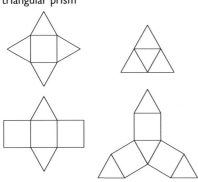

3. a)

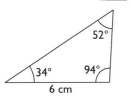

52°
34°   94°
6 cm

4. a) Go 11 miles West and 5 miles North to point B.
Go 6 miles West and 7 miles South to point C.
Go 2 miles East and 5 miles South to point D.
Go 4 miles East and 5 miles North to point E.
Go 5 miles East and 11 miles South to point F.
Go 7 miles East and 2 miles North to point G.
Go 6 miles West and 6 miles North to point H.
Go 3 miles West and 2 miles North to point I.

b) Go 15 miles East and 6 miles South

5. a) A and B

b)

c) (i) 2:

(ii) 8:

6. a) A
b) 80°
c) 95°
d) 97° to 111°

7. a) (1, 5), (1, 3), (1, 2), (1, 1), (1, 0), (1, −1), (1, −2), (1, −3), (1, −4), (1, −5).
(−2, −2) and (4, −2) give right-angled triangles which are also isosceles.

b) E.g.

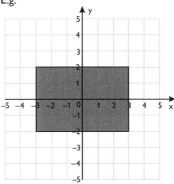

Any shape that's symmetrical about both the x- and y-axis is also correct.

c) (i) E.g. the y-coordinate stays the same but the x-coordinate changes sign.
(ii) E.g. the x-coordinate stays the same but the y-coordinate changes sign.
(iii) E.g. both the x-coordinate and y-coordinate change sign.

Section 8 — Statistics

Pages 155-156: Solving Problems with Line Graphs — 1

Set A

1. $12
2. $6
3. $15
4. $7.50
5. £2
6. £6
7. £60
8.

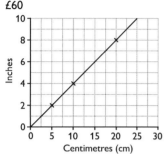

9. 10 inches
10. 15 cm
11. 5 inches
12. 7.5 cm

Set B

1.

Route	A	B	C	D
Kilometres	8	16	24	12
Miles	5	10	15	7.5

2. 64 km
3. 100 miles
4.

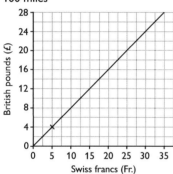

5. 10 Fr
6. 30 Fr
7. £12
8. 17.50 Fr
9. £26
10. 50 Fr
11. 150 Fr
12. £200
13. £2400

Set C

1.

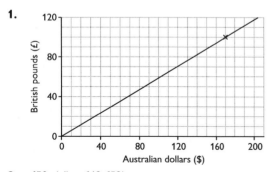

2. £50 (allow £48-£52)
3. $51 (allow $50-$52)
4. £41 (allow £40-£42)
5. $162 (allow $160-$164)
6. 50 miles
7. 320 km
8. 500 miles
9. 192 km
10. 2500 miles
11. Smaller, the graph would give 1600 km.

Pages 157-158: Solving Problems with Line Graphs — 2

Set A

1-4.

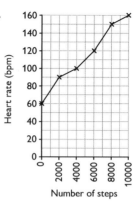

5. 4000
6. 100 bpm
7. 4 minutes
8. 4 °C
9. 12 minutes

Set B

1.

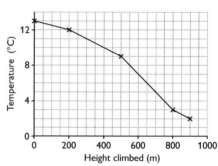

2. 10 °C
3. 7 °C
4.

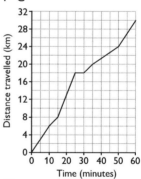

5. 60
6. 18, 5
7. 25
8. 3

Set C

1. The horizontal and vertical axes only have 2 values each.
2.

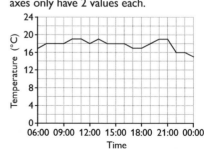

3. 21:00, 22:00
4. 1.5 kg
5. £1.50
6. £0.50
7. Best Buffet

Page 159: Statistics — Review 1

1. 40 pints
2. 2.5 gallons
3. 80 pints
4. 8 pints
5. ¥1400
6. £5
7. £50 *(allow £49-£51)*
8. ¥14 000
9. 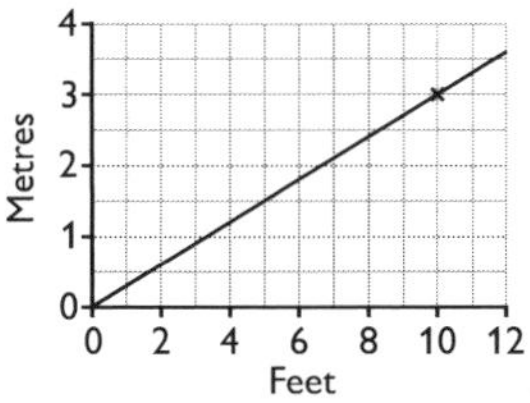

10. 2.5 m
11. 6 feet

12-13. 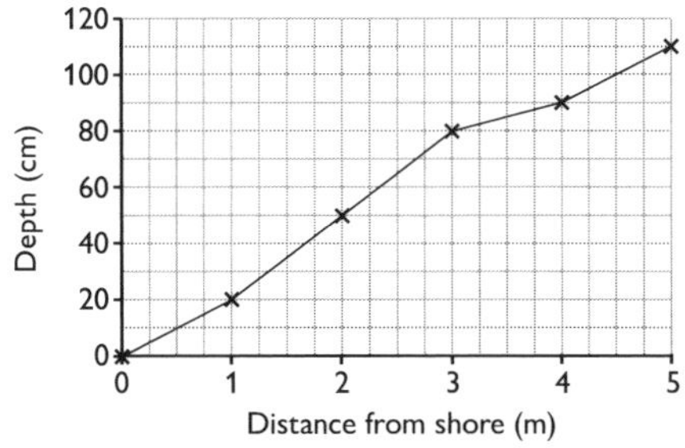

14. 80 cm
15. 50 cm
16. 85 cm
17. 95 cm
18. 0.5 m
19. 1.7 m *(allow 1.6-1.8 m)*
20. 2000
21. 55 seconds
22. 1250
23. 15 seconds

Pages 160-161: Pie Charts

Set A

1. cereal
2. fruit
3. false
4. true
5. 200°
6. 90°
7. 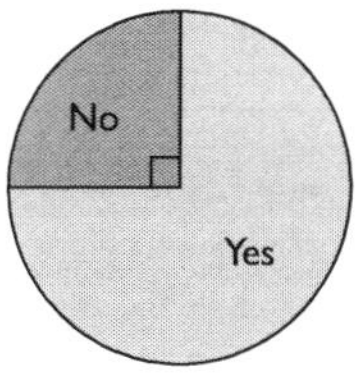

8. 10, 10
9. 10, 200
10. 10, 100
11. 10, 60

Set B

1. green
2. 30°
3. 50%
4. $\frac{5}{12}$
5.

	Broken	Not broken
Number	10	50
Sector angle	60°	300°

6. 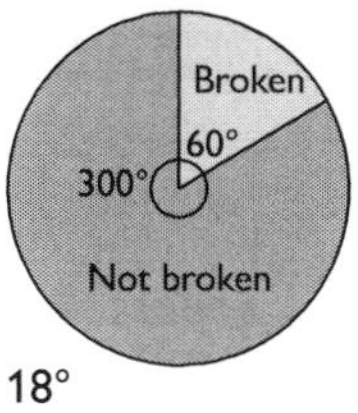

7. 18°
8. 144°
9. 2
10. £1000 angle: 80°
    £100 angle: 120°
    £1 angle: 160°
11. 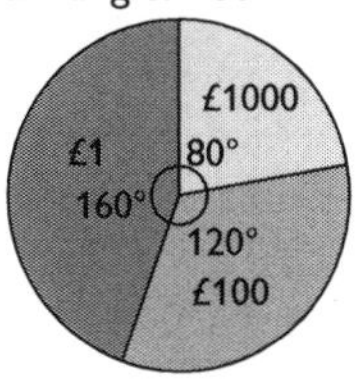

Set C

1. brown, blonde, grey
2. 10°
3. $\frac{1}{6}$
4. $\frac{5}{18}$
5. $\frac{5}{9}$
6.

Eye colour	Brown	Blue	Green	Hazel
No. of people	10	15	9	2
Sector angle	100°	150°	90°	20°

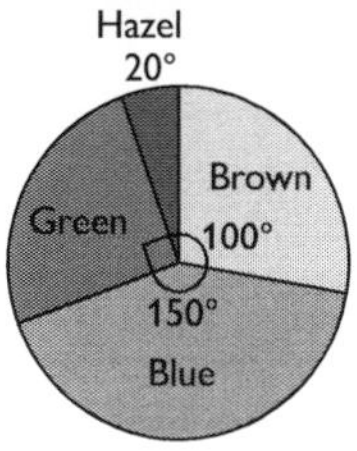

7. False: the same proportion write with their left hand, but there are more girls, so there are more girls who write with their left hand.
8. True: the proportion is a quarter for boys and girls, so it doesn't change for all Year 6 children.
9. False: the same proportion write with their right hand, but there are fewer boys, so fewer boys than girls write with their right hand.
10. 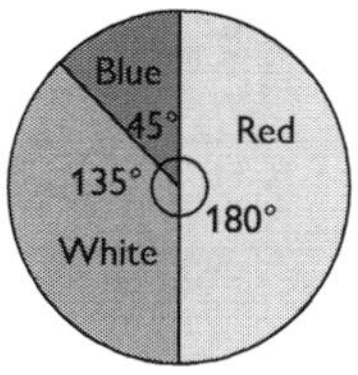

Pages 162-163: Solving Problems with Pie Charts

Set A

1. 24
2. 6
3. 3
4. 45°
5. 2
6. 30°
7. 80
8. 20
9. 48
10. 8
11. 28

Set B

1. 20
2. 6
3. 9
4. 1st: 5,
   2nd: 15,
   3rd: 20
5. 72
6. Saturday: the number of lollies sold was the same on both days, so on Saturday three times as many cones were sold, but on Sunday only two times as many cones were sold.
7. 100
8. 200

Set C

1. 48
2. 12
3. 2
4. £15
5. 48
6. 20
7. £10
8. A quarter of 50 g is 12.5 g and a sixth of 30 g is 5 g, so approximately 7.5 g more.

Page 164: Mean — 1

Set A

1. 5
2. 11
3. 41
4. 7
5. 11
6. 8
7. 22
8. 6
9. 20
10. 10
11. 4 m
12. 12 years
13. £25

Set B

1. 40
2. 30
3. 190
4. 40
5. 220
6. 2000
7. 16
8. £18
9. £140
10. £2200
11. 80p
12. 9 years
13. 6 m

Set C

1. 23
2. 2001
3. 147
4. 0.06
5. 2
6. 2.5
7. 5
8. 15
9. 11
10. 5.6
11. 3
12. 38 kg
13. 4 kg

Page 165: Mean — 2

Set A

1. 5
2. 40
3. 50
4. 50
5. 40 years
6. 120
7. 35 g
8. 8
9. 11
10. 19
11. 5

Set B

1. 13 kg
2. 520 cm
3. 12
4. 70
5. 16
6. higher
7. 19
8. 85
9. 3410
10. 1.2

Set C

1. 120
2. 107
3. 1.3
4. 4.60
5. 11.8 s
6. 55 g
7. 30 cm
8. red: 17cm, blue: 13 cm

Page 166: Statistics — Review 2

1. tulips
2. 50%
3. $\frac{1}{6}$
4. 30°
5. 2°
6.

	brazil	cashew	peanut	Total
Number	15	45	120	180
Sector angle	30°	90°	240°	360°

7.

8. 280
9. 140
10. 70
11. 70
12. 760
13. 300
14. 10
15. 60
16. 90
17. 10
18. 80
19. 7
20. 16
21. 11
22. 28
23. 40
24. 200
25. 2200
26. 2
27. 60
28. 2
29. 166 cm
30. 165
31. 50
32. 43
33. 10

Pages 167-168: Statistics — Challenges

1. a) B and D
   b)

	green	purple	yellow	red	blue
Number	75	150	75	100	200

2. a) 1200 Ft
   b)

graph: y-axis Hungarian forint (Ft) 0 to 2000, x-axis Croatian kuna (kn) 0 to 50, with point marked at (30, 1200)

3. No: she needs a total score of 450, so she needs to score a total of 210 in the History and Music tests. This isn't possible since each test is out of 100.
4. a) 10 grams
   b) (i) 10 ounces
      (ii) 50 ounces
5. Beth, Dinah, Ed and Fin
6. a) SlowCoach: C
      CoachPotato: B
      Coach-to-Coast: A
   b) Company A: £55
      Company B: £35
      Company C: £45
   c) 67 km to 190 km *(allow +/− 2 km on each bound)*

M6PBA21